From The Nation's #1 Educational I

Grade

Math

CONTENTS

Credits
Author:
Thomas J. Richards - Mathematics Teacher; Lamar
Junior-Senior High School; Lamar, Missouri

Cover Design & Illustration:
Beachcomber Studio

McGraw-Hill Consumer Products Editorial/Production Team:
Vincent F. Douglas, B.S. and M. Ed.
Tracy R. Paulus
Jennifer Blashkiw Pawley

Photo Credits:
Andy Stack/Tony Stone Images, 80

McGraw-Hill
Consumer Products

*A Division of The **McGraw·Hill** Companies*

1-57768-416-8   1 2 3 4 5 6 7 8 9 10 QPD 04 03 02 01 00 99

Lesson 1 Addition and Subtraction

Add or subtract.

	a	*b*	*c*	*d*	*e*	*f*
1.	32 + 6	5 +48	23 +35	47 +26	89 +50	78 +57
2.	58 −3	72 −21	47 −38	159 −93	143 −85	202 −37
3.	523 +364	428 +537	683 +194	385 +276	483 +629	753 +869
4.	783 −502	926 −418	564 −283	1925 −137	2436 −648	1926 −928
5.	5231 +3468	4661 +2179	3157 +6930	2087 +9237	4281 +6759	
6.	8426 −3312	7531 −3452	8426 −2756	13041 −9158	25308 −8499	
7.	63125 +10420	42163 +45387	28135 +47385	61702 +28715	37839 +57893	
8.	72519 −30418	83162 −35087	52083 −41839	98035 −68746	63613 −55895	
9.	23 34 +42	426 709 +358	4216 5384 +2196	22514 43868 +21706	82965 372 +1451	

Problem Solving

Answer each question. Use the space at the right to work each problem.

1. In a contest, Cara earned 758 points. Kelley earned 929 points. Bill earned 1,356 points. How many points did the two girls earn?

   Are you to add or subtract? _____

   How many points did the two girls earn? _____

   1.

2. In problem 1, how many more points did Bill earn than Kelley?

   Are you to add or subtract? _____
   How many more points did
     Bill earn than Kelley? _____

   2.

3. In problem 1, how many points did all three people earn?

   Are you to add or subtract? _____

   How many points did all three earn? _____

   3.

4. This month 32,526 people visited the museum. Last month 28,831 people visited the museum. How many more people visited the museum this month than last month?

   Are you to add or subtract? _____
   How many more people visited the
     museum this month than last month? _____

   4.

5. In problem 4, how many people visited the museum during the two months?

   Are you to add or subtract? _____
   How many people visited the
     museum during the two months? _____

   5.

6. At the beginning of last year 52,116 cars were registered. There were 4,913 new cars registered the first six months and 3,085 the second six months. How many cars were registered at the end of the year?

   Are you to add or subtract? _____

   How many cars were registered
     at the end of the year? _____

   6.

4

Lesson 2 Multiplication

Multiply.

	a	*b*	*c*	*d*	*e*	*f*	*g*	*h*
1.	4 ×0	2 ×0	8 ×0	1 ×0	7 ×1	6 ×1	1 ×1	5 ×1
2.	8 ×2	2 ×2	4 ×2	7 ×2	6 ×2	5 ×2	3 ×2	9 ×2
3.	9 ×3	7 ×3	5 ×3	0 ×3	1 ×3	6 ×3	4 ×3	3 ×3
4.	4 ×4	3 ×4	5 ×4	8 ×4	7 ×4	0 ×4	9 ×4	1 ×4
5.	8 ×5	2 ×5	7 ×5	5 ×5	4 ×5	3 ×5	1 ×5	0 ×5
6.	8 ×6	2 ×6	9 ×6	7 ×6	6 ×6	5 ×6	1 ×6	3 ×6
7.	9 ×7	7 ×7	6 ×7	0 ×7	1 ×7	5 ×7	8 ×7	4 ×7
8.	0 ×8	5 ×8	8 ×8	9 ×8	4 ×8	3 ×8	6 ×8	7 ×8
9.	3 ×9	9 ×9	8 ×9	1 ×9	2 ×9	7 ×9	6 ×9	4 ×9

Lesson 3 Division

Divide.

	a	b	c	d	e	f	g	h
1.	$1\overline{)2}$	$1\overline{)3}$	$1\overline{)5}$	$1\overline{)4}$	$1\overline{)6}$	$1\overline{)9}$	$1\overline{)8}$	$1\overline{)1}$
2.	$2\overline{)18}$	$2\overline{)12}$	$2\overline{)14}$	$2\overline{)16}$	$2\overline{)8}$	$2\overline{)10}$	$2\overline{)4}$	$2\overline{)2}$
3.	$3\overline{)0}$	$3\overline{)15}$	$3\overline{)9}$	$3\overline{)12}$	$3\overline{)24}$	$3\overline{)18}$	$3\overline{)3}$	$3\overline{)21}$
4.	$4\overline{)20}$	$4\overline{)8}$	$4\overline{)4}$	$4\overline{)12}$	$4\overline{)32}$	$4\overline{)24}$	$4\overline{)36}$	$4\overline{)16}$
5.	$5\overline{)30}$	$5\overline{)45}$	$5\overline{)0}$	$5\overline{)10}$	$5\overline{)25}$	$5\overline{)15}$	$5\overline{)40}$	$5\overline{)5}$
6.	$6\overline{)30}$	$6\overline{)24}$	$6\overline{)42}$	$6\overline{)6}$	$6\overline{)12}$	$6\overline{)36}$	$6\overline{)54}$	$6\overline{)48}$
7.	$7\overline{)0}$	$7\overline{)21}$	$7\overline{)14}$	$7\overline{)56}$	$7\overline{)49}$	$7\overline{)63}$	$7\overline{)35}$	$7\overline{)28}$
8.	$8\overline{)16}$	$8\overline{)0}$	$8\overline{)56}$	$8\overline{)72}$	$8\overline{)48}$	$8\overline{)32}$	$8\overline{)24}$	$8\overline{)40}$
9.	$9\overline{)45}$	$9\overline{)27}$	$9\overline{)36}$	$9\overline{)63}$	$9\overline{)9}$	$9\overline{)81}$	$9\overline{)0}$	$9\overline{)54}$

Lesson 4 Multiplication

Multiply 7 ones by 5.	Multiply 1 ten by 5. Add the 3 tens.	Multiply 8 hundreds by 5.	Multiply 9 thousands by 5. Add the 4 thousands.

$$
\begin{array}{cc}
\overset{3}{9\,8\,1\,7} & 7 \\
\times 5 & \times 5 \\
\hline
5 & 35 \\
\end{array}
$$

$$
\begin{array}{cc}
\overset{3}{9\,8\,1\,7} & 10 \\
\times 5 & \times 5 \\
\hline
8\,5 & 50 \\
& +30 \\
\hline
& 80 \\
\end{array}
$$

$$
\begin{array}{cc}
\overset{4}{9}\overset{3}{8}1\,7 & 800 \\
\times 5 & \times 5 \\
\hline
0\,8\,5 & 4000 \\
\end{array}
$$

$$
\begin{array}{cc}
\overset{4}{9}\overset{3}{8}1\,7 & 9000 \\
\times 5 & \times 5 \\
\hline
4\,9\,0\,8\,5 & 45000 \\
& +4000 \\
\hline
& 49000 \\
\end{array}
$$

Multiply.

	a	b	c	d	e
1.	3 2 ×3	2 3 ×4	8 2 ×3	7 8 ×8	9 5 ×6
2.	4 2 1 ×2	1 2 3 ×4	2 4 1 ×3	5 0 1 ×5	1 5 9 ×6
3.	7 8 3 ×3	5 3 8 ×8	7 6 2 ×5	9 5 4 ×7	4 7 3 ×9
4.	1 0 3 3 ×2	3 2 1 6 ×3	3 1 7 2 ×3	5 0 1 4 ×2	3 2 5 7 ×3
5.	1 4 7 8 ×6	5 7 3 8 ×7	4 8 2 6 ×9	5 3 8 4 ×6	7 0 8 3 ×5

Lesson 5   Multiplication

Multiply 4567 by 1.	**Multiply 4567 by 20.**	Multiply 4567 by 300.	
4567 ×321 ――― 4567	4567 ×321 ――― 4567 91340	4567 ×321 ――― 4567 91340 1370100	4567 ×321 ――― 4567 ⎤ 91340 ⎬ Add. 1370100 ⎦ ――――― 1,466,007

Multiply.

1.

$$\begin{array}{r} 57 \\ \times 21 \\ \hline \end{array} \qquad \begin{array}{r} 48 \\ \times 32 \\ \hline \end{array} \qquad \begin{array}{r} 75 \\ \times 63 \\ \hline \end{array} \qquad \begin{array}{r} 135 \\ \times 48 \\ \hline \end{array} \qquad \begin{array}{r} 276 \\ \times 42 \\ \hline \end{array}$$

2.

$$\begin{array}{r} 531 \\ \times 27 \\ \hline \end{array} \qquad \begin{array}{r} 835 \\ \times 92 \\ \hline \end{array} \qquad \begin{array}{r} 1864 \\ \times 27 \\ \hline \end{array} \qquad \begin{array}{r} 3186 \\ \times 54 \\ \hline \end{array} \qquad \begin{array}{r} 7083 \\ \times 92 \\ \hline \end{array}$$

3.

$$\begin{array}{r} 413 \\ \times 214 \\ \hline \end{array} \qquad \begin{array}{r} 564 \\ \times 532 \\ \hline \end{array} \qquad \begin{array}{r} 217 \\ \times 416 \\ \hline \end{array} \qquad \begin{array}{r} 908 \\ \times 592 \\ \hline \end{array}$$

4.

$$\begin{array}{r} 1564 \\ \times 795 \\ \hline \end{array} \qquad \begin{array}{r} 3827 \\ \times 630 \\ \hline \end{array} \qquad \begin{array}{r} 9216 \\ \times 205 \\ \hline \end{array} \qquad \begin{array}{r} 5043 \\ \times 684 \\ \hline \end{array}$$

Problem Solving

Answer each question. Use the space at the right to work each problem.

1. Each box weighs 28 kilograms. What is the weight of 35 such boxes?

   Each box weighs _____ kilograms.

   There are _____ boxes in all.

   The total weight is _____ kilograms.

   1.

2. There are 19 carpenters working for a construction firm. Each worked 47 hours last week. What is the total number of hours they worked last week?

   Each carpenter worked _____ hours.

   There are _____ carpenters in all.

   _____ hours were worked.

   2.

3. The production schedule estimates that 321 machines can be produced each week. At that rate, how many machines can be produced in 52 weeks?

   There are _____ machines scheduled to be produced each week.

   There are _____ weeks.

   _____ machines can be produced in 52 weeks.

   3.

4. The rail distance between Los Angeles and New York is 3,257 miles. How many miles would a train travel if it made 32 one-way trips between these two cities?

   The train would travel _____ miles.

   4.

5. There are 731 cases of zoopers in the warehouse. Each case contains 144 zoopers. How many zoopers are in the warehouse?

   There are _____ zoopers in the warehouse.

   5.

6. There are 1,440 minutes in one day. How many minutes are in 365 days?

   There are _____ minutes in 365 days.

   6.

9

Lesson 6 Division

Study how to divide 2074 by 6.

×	100	200	300	400
6	600	1200	1800	2400

2074 is between 1800 and 2400, so 2074 ÷ 6 is between 300 and 400. The hundreds digit is 3.

```
     3
6) 2074
   1800      (300 × 6)
   ────
    274    Subtract.
```

×	10	20	30	40	50
6	60	120	180	240	300

274 is between 240 and 300, so 274 ÷ 6 is between 40 and 50. The tens digit is 4.

```
    34
6) 2074
   1800
   ────
    274
    240      (40 × 6)
    ───
     34    Subtract.
```

×	1	2	3	4	5	6	7
6	6	12	18	24	30	36	42

34 is between 30 and 36, so 34 ÷ 6 is between 5 and 6. The ones digit is 5.

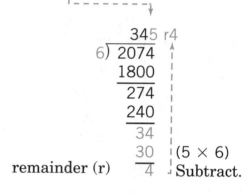

```
                    345 r4
              6) 2074
                 1800
                 ────
                  274
                  240
                  ───
                   34
                   30    (5 × 6)
       remainder (r)  ──
                    4    Subtract.
```

Divide.

	a	b	c	d	e
1.	4) 9 2	3) 5 8	3) 7 2	4) 7 7	6) 8 1 0
2.	3) 2 2 5	6) 5 9 0	6) 8 0 8 0	9) 4 7 3 9	6) 4 2 5 4

10

Problem Solving

Answer each question. Use the space at the right to work each problem.

1. There are 5 people at each table. Two people are standing. There are 92 people in the room. How many tables are there?

   There are _____ people in the room.

   There are _____ people at each table.

   There are _____ tables in the room.

1.

2. Three people earned 774 points in a contest. Suppose each person earned the same number of points. How many points did each person earn?

   Each person earned _____ points.

2.

3. As each new car comes off an assembly line, it receives 8 gallons of gasoline. How many new cars can receive gasoline from a tank containing 2,440 gallons?

   _____ new cars can receive gasoline.

3.

4. Four baseballs are put in each box. How many boxes are needed to package 273 baseballs? How many baseballs would be left?

   _____ boxes are needed.

   _____ baseball would be left.

4.

5. A train travels 6,516 miles to make a round-trip between New York and Los Angeles. How many miles would the train travel from Los Angeles to New York?

   The train would travel _____ miles.

5.

6. Each carton holds 8 bottles. How many full cartons could be filled with 3,075 bottles? How many bottles would be left over?

   _____ cartons could be filled.

   _____ bottles would be left over.

6.

Lesson 7   Division

Study how to divide 28888 by 95.

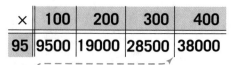

×	100	200	300	400
95	9500	19000	28500	38000

28888 is between 28500
and 38000, so 28888 ÷ 95
is between 300 and 400.
The hundreds digit
is 3.

```
       3
95) 28888
    28500  (300×95)
      388  Subtract.
```

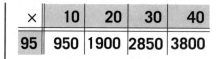

×	10	20	30	40
95	950	1900	2850	3800

Since 388 is less than
950, the tens digit
is 0.

```
      30
95) 28888
    28500
      388
        0  (0×95)
      388  Subtract.
```

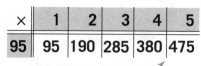

×	1	2	3	4	5
95	95	190	285	380	475

388 is between 380 and
475, so 388 ÷ 95 is
between 4 and 5.
The ones digit is 4.

```
     304 r8
95) 28888
    28500
      388
        0
      388
      380  (4×95)
        8  Subtract.
```

Divide.

a　　　　b　　　　c　　　　d　　　　e

1. 25) 8 1 0   33) 8 9 1   18) 8 1 9   27) 7 2 7   75) 6 9 0 0

2. 54) 7 6 9 5   28) 9 6 9 8   98) 3 4 9 3 7   75) 3 9 4 0 0   42) 1 4 7 4 2

Problem Solving

Solve each problem. Use the space at the right to work each problem.

1. There are 988 units to be shipped. Each crate will hold 26 units. How many crates will be needed to ship all the units?

   There are _____ units to be shipped.

   Each crate will hold _____ units.

   _____ crates will be needed.

2. Mr. Lodey has 987 parts to pack. He will pack 24 parts in each box. How many boxes will he need? How many parts will be left over?

   He will need _____ boxes.

   He will have _____ parts left over.

3. A bank considers 30 days to be a month. How many months would there be in 9,295 days? How many days would be left over?

   There would be _____ months.

   There would be _____ days left over.

4. During a two-week period, 75 employees worked a total of 5,625 hours. Each employee worked the same number of hours. How many hours did each employee work?

   Each employee worked _____ hours.

5. There are 76 sections with a total of 17,100 seats in the new stadium. Each section has the same number of seats. How many seats are in each section?

   There are _____ seats in each section.

6. Three dozen grapefruit are packed in a case. How many cases would be needed to pack 27,100 grapefruit? How many grapefruit would be left over?

   _____ cases would be needed.

   _____ grapefruit would be left over.

1.	2.
3.	4.
5.	6.

Lesson 8 Fractions

$\frac{2}{3}$ ← **numerator** ← - - - - - number of parts colored - - - - → **numerator** → $\frac{1}{4}$

 ← **denominator** ← - number of parts of the same size - → **denominator** →

$\frac{2}{3}$ of the triangle is colored. $\qquad\qquad\qquad\qquad$ $\frac{1}{4}$ of the square is colored.

Write the fraction that tells how much of each figure is colored.

	a	*b*	*c*	*d*
1.	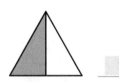			
2.	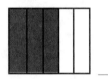			

Draw a line segment between each fraction and number word that names the same number.

	a		*b*	
3.	one-half	$\frac{4}{5}$	three-eighths	$\frac{7}{9}$
4.	two-thirds	$\frac{3}{4}$	four-sevenths	$\frac{3}{8}$
5.	three-fourths	$\frac{2}{3}$	three-sevenths	$\frac{3}{7}$
6.	four-fifths	$\frac{1}{2}$	seven-eighths	$\frac{4}{7}$
7.	five-sixths	$\frac{5}{6}$	seven-ninths	$\frac{7}{8}$

Write a fraction for each of the following.

	a	*b*
8.	numerator 4, denominator 7 ____	three-fifths ____
9.	numerator 5, denominator 8 ____	two-sevenths ____
10.	denominator 10, numerator 9 ____	four-ninths ____

Lesson 9   Mixed Numerals

$\dfrac{13}{4}$ means $\begin{cases} 13 \div 4 \\ \text{or} \\ 4\overline{)13} \end{cases}$

$\begin{array}{r} 3\frac{1}{4} \\ 4\overline{)13} \\ \underline{12} \\ 1 \end{array} \rightarrow 1 \div 4 = \dfrac{1}{4}$

$3\frac{1}{4}$ is a short way to write $3 + \frac{1}{4}$.

$3\frac{1}{4}$ is a **mixed numeral**.

Complete the following.

	a	b	c	d
1.	$3\frac{1}{5} = 3 + \underline{\ \ }$	$4\frac{1}{2} = \underline{\ \ } + \frac{1}{2}$	$3\frac{3}{4} = \underline{\ \ } + \underline{\ \ }$	$9 + \frac{1}{3} = \underline{\ \ }$
2.	$4\frac{2}{3} = 4 + \underline{\ \ }$	$5\frac{3}{7} = \underline{\ \ } + \frac{3}{7}$	$6\frac{2}{5} = \underline{\ \ } + \underline{\ \ }$	$8 + \frac{7}{8} = \underline{\ \ }$
3.	$5\frac{1}{8} = 5 + \underline{\ \ }$	$2\frac{1}{6} = \underline{\ \ } + \frac{1}{6}$	$3\frac{1}{3} = \underline{\ \ } + \underline{\ \ }$	$5 + \frac{3}{7} = \underline{\ \ }$

Change each fraction to a mixed numeral.

	a	b	c
4.	$\dfrac{5}{2}$	$\dfrac{9}{5}$	$\dfrac{7}{2}$
5.	$\dfrac{9}{4}$	$\dfrac{6}{5}$	$\dfrac{8}{3}$
6.	$\dfrac{14}{3}$	$\dfrac{10}{3}$	$\dfrac{17}{5}$

Tell whether each of the following is *less than 1, equal to 1,* or *greater than 1.*

	a	b	c
7.	$\dfrac{7}{8}$ _____	$\dfrac{5}{4}$ _____	$\dfrac{6}{6}$ _____
8.	$\dfrac{2}{3}$ _____	$\dfrac{12}{12}$ _____	$\dfrac{11}{10}$ _____
9.	$\dfrac{1}{9}$ _____	$\dfrac{12}{9}$ _____	$\dfrac{10}{5}$ _____

Lesson 10   Addition

$$\frac{2}{5} + \frac{1}{5} = \frac{2+1}{5}$$ Add the numerators.

$$= \frac{3}{5}$$ Use the same denominator.

$$\begin{array}{r} \frac{2}{5} \\ + \frac{1}{5} \\ \hline \frac{3}{5} \end{array}$$

$$\frac{3}{10} + \frac{4}{10} + \frac{2}{10} = \frac{3+4+2}{10}$$

$$= \frac{9}{10}$$

$$\begin{array}{r} \frac{3}{10} \\ \frac{4}{10} \\ + \frac{2}{10} \\ \hline \frac{9}{10} \end{array}$$

Add.

	a	*b*	*c*	*d*
1.	$\frac{3}{5} + \frac{1}{5} =$	$\frac{4}{8} + \frac{3}{8} =$	$\frac{2}{7} + \frac{2}{7} =$	$\frac{1}{5} + \frac{2}{5} + \frac{1}{5} =$
2.	$\frac{3}{6} + \frac{2}{6} =$	$\frac{1}{7} + \frac{3}{7} =$	$\frac{2}{8} + \frac{1}{8} =$	$\frac{1}{4} + \frac{1}{4} + \frac{1}{4} =$
3.	$\frac{3}{10} + \frac{4}{10} =$	$\frac{4}{12} + \frac{1}{12} =$	$\frac{5}{11} + \frac{4}{11} =$	$\frac{2}{15} + \frac{2}{15} + \frac{7}{15} =$

	a	*b*	*c*	*d*	*e*	*f*
4.	$\begin{array}{r}\frac{4}{6}\\ +\frac{1}{6}\\ \hline\end{array}$	$\begin{array}{r}\frac{3}{8}\\ +\frac{4}{8}\\ \hline\end{array}$	$\begin{array}{r}\frac{1}{7}\\ +\frac{2}{7}\\ \hline\end{array}$	$\begin{array}{r}\frac{3}{10}\\ +\frac{6}{10}\\ \hline\end{array}$	$\begin{array}{r}\frac{7}{12}\\ +\frac{4}{12}\\ \hline\end{array}$	$\begin{array}{r}\frac{3}{11}\\ +\frac{1}{11}\\ \hline\end{array}$
5.	$\begin{array}{r}\frac{1}{5}\\ \frac{1}{5}\\ +\frac{1}{5}\\ \hline\end{array}$	$\begin{array}{r}\frac{2}{7}\\ \frac{3}{7}\\ +\frac{1}{7}\\ \hline\end{array}$	$\begin{array}{r}\frac{2}{8}\\ \frac{1}{8}\\ +\frac{2}{8}\\ \hline\end{array}$	$\begin{array}{r}\frac{4}{10}\\ \frac{1}{10}\\ +\frac{2}{10}\\ \hline\end{array}$	$\begin{array}{r}\frac{3}{15}\\ \frac{4}{15}\\ +\frac{4}{15}\\ \hline\end{array}$	$\begin{array}{r}\frac{1}{12}\\ \frac{4}{12}\\ +\frac{2}{12}\\ \hline\end{array}$

Lesson 11   Mixed Numerals to Fractions

$4\frac{2}{3} = \frac{(3 \times 4) + 2}{3}$ Multiply the denominator by the whole number and add the numerator. $3\frac{1}{6} = \frac{(6 \times 3) + 1}{6}$

$= \frac{12 + 2}{3}$ **Use the same denominator.** $= \frac{18 + 1}{6}$

$= \frac{14}{3}$ $= \frac{19}{6}$

Change each mixed numeral to a fraction.

	a	b	c
1.	$2\frac{5}{8}$	$2\frac{3}{5}$	$3\frac{2}{3}$
2.	$3\frac{7}{10}$	$10\frac{2}{3}$	$14\frac{1}{2}$
3.	$6\frac{7}{8}$	$5\frac{9}{10}$	$13\frac{5}{12}$
4.	$4\frac{5}{6}$	$7\frac{3}{4}$	$8\frac{11}{12}$

Lesson 12   Multiplication

Multiply the numerators.

$$\frac{2}{3} \times \frac{1}{5} = \frac{2 \times 1}{3 \times 5} = \frac{2}{15}$$

Multiply the denominators.

$$\frac{1}{2} \times \frac{3}{4} = \frac{1 \times 3}{2 \times 4}$$
$$= \frac{3}{8}$$

$$\frac{2}{5} \times \frac{1}{3} = \frac{2 \times 1}{5 \times 3}$$
$$= \frac{2}{15}$$

Multiply.

	a	*b*	*c*	*d*
1.	$\frac{1}{2} \times \frac{1}{3}$	$\frac{3}{4} \times \frac{1}{2}$	$\frac{1}{3} \times \frac{1}{4}$	$\frac{3}{5} \times \frac{1}{2}$
2.	$\frac{3}{5} \times \frac{3}{4}$	$\frac{4}{7} \times \frac{3}{5}$	$\frac{4}{5} \times \frac{2}{3}$	$\frac{3}{8} \times \frac{5}{7}$
3.	$\frac{2}{3} \times \frac{4}{5}$	$\frac{1}{8} \times \frac{1}{2}$	$\frac{5}{7} \times \frac{3}{4}$	$\frac{3}{5} \times \frac{7}{8}$
4.	$\frac{6}{7} \times \frac{3}{5}$	$\frac{2}{9} \times \frac{1}{3}$	$\frac{5}{8} \times \frac{3}{7}$	$\frac{2}{7} \times \frac{3}{5}$
5.	$\frac{7}{8} \times \frac{7}{8}$	$\frac{2}{3} \times \frac{2}{3}$	$\frac{4}{9} \times \frac{2}{3}$	$\frac{4}{5} \times \frac{6}{7}$
6.	$\frac{8}{9} \times \frac{5}{7}$	$\frac{5}{8} \times \frac{1}{3}$	$\frac{5}{6} \times \frac{5}{7}$	$\frac{3}{8} \times \frac{5}{8}$

Lesson 13   Simplest Form

A fraction is in simplest form when its numerator and denominator have no common factors, except 1.

Divide 12 and 15 by their greatest common factor.

$$\frac{12}{15} = \frac{12 \div 3}{15 \div 3} = \frac{4}{5}$$

The simplest form for $\frac{12}{15}$ is ___$\frac{4}{5}$___.

A mixed numeral is in simplest form when its fraction is in simplest form and names a number less than 1.

Divide 4 and 6 by their greatest common factor.

$$3\frac{4}{6} = 3 + \frac{4 \div 2}{6 \div 2}$$
$$= 3 + \frac{2}{3}$$
$$= 3\frac{2}{3}$$

The simplest form for $3\frac{4}{6}$ is ___$3\frac{2}{3}$___.

Change each of the following to simplest form.

	a	b	c
1.	$\frac{8}{10}$	$\frac{10}{20}$	$\frac{14}{21}$
2.	$2\frac{4}{8}$	$3\frac{6}{9}$	$5\frac{8}{10}$
3.	$\frac{12}{18}$	$5\frac{9}{12}$	$\frac{15}{18}$
4.	$6\frac{8}{12}$	$\frac{25}{30}$	$3\frac{12}{16}$
5.	$\frac{24}{30}$	$3\frac{14}{18}$	$\frac{16}{32}$

Lesson 14 Multiplication

$$\frac{1}{2} \times \frac{3}{4} = \frac{1 \times 3}{2 \times 4}$$
$$= \frac{3}{8}$$

Is $\frac{3}{8}$ in simplest form? ____yes____

$$\frac{4}{5} \times \frac{1}{6} = \frac{4 \times 1}{5 \times 6}$$
$$= \frac{4}{30} \dashrightarrow \frac{4}{30} = \frac{4 + 2}{30 + 2}$$
$$= \frac{2}{15} \dashleftarrow = \frac{2}{15}$$

Is $\frac{4}{30}$ in simplest form? ____no____
Is $\frac{2}{15}$ in simplest form? ____yes____

Write each answer in simplest form.

	a	b	c	d
1.	$\frac{1}{2} \times \frac{3}{5}$	$\frac{2}{3} \times \frac{4}{5}$	$\frac{2}{3} \times \frac{2}{3}$	$\frac{5}{6} \times \frac{1}{7}$
2.	$\frac{3}{4} \times \frac{4}{5}$	$\frac{5}{6} \times \frac{2}{3}$	$\frac{6}{7} \times \frac{2}{3}$	$\frac{3}{5} \times \frac{4}{9}$
3.	$\frac{5}{6} \times \frac{2}{5}$	$\frac{4}{5} \times \frac{5}{6}$	$\frac{3}{8} \times \frac{2}{3}$	$\frac{2}{10} \times \frac{5}{6}$
4.	$\frac{6}{5} \times \frac{3}{8}$	$\frac{9}{10} \times \frac{5}{12}$	$\frac{8}{9} \times \frac{3}{10}$	$\frac{5}{6} \times \frac{9}{10}$
5.	$\frac{4}{7} \times \frac{5}{6}$	$\frac{3}{8} \times \frac{7}{10}$	$\frac{9}{10} \times \frac{5}{9}$	$\frac{6}{7} \times \frac{9}{10}$

Problem Solving

Solve. Write each answer in simplest form. Use the space at the right to work each problem.

1. The Urbans had $\frac{3}{4}$ gallon of milk. One-half of this was used for dinner. How much milk was used for dinner? ($\frac{1}{2}$ of $\frac{3}{4} = \frac{1}{2} \times \frac{3}{4}$)

   1.

   _____ gallon was used for dinner.

2. Keara read $\frac{4}{5}$ of a book. Two-thirds of that reading was done at school. How much of the book did she read at school?

   2.

   She read _____ of the book at school.

3. Tricia lives $\frac{4}{5}$ mile from work. One morning she ran $\frac{1}{2}$ of the distance to work. How far did Tricia run?

   3.

   Tricia ran _____ mile.

4. Three-fourths of a room has been painted. Joseph did $\frac{2}{3}$ of the painting. How much of the room did Joseph paint?

   4.

   Joseph painted _____ of the room.

5. A truck was carrying $\frac{3}{4}$ ton of sand. One-third of the sand was put into barrels. How much sand was put into barrels?

   5.

   _____ ton of sand was put into barrels.

6. Carrie had a rope that was $\frac{2}{3}$ yard long. She used $\frac{1}{2}$ of it. How much rope did she use?

   6.

   _____ yard of rope was used.

7. One-fourth of the people in the room have blue eyes. Two-thirds of the blue-eyed people have blond hair. What part of the people in the room have blond hair and blue eyes?

   7.

   _____ have blond hair and blue eyes.

Lesson 15   Multiplication

$$4 \times \frac{5}{6} = \frac{4}{1} \times \frac{5}{6}$$

Rename whole numbers and mixed numerals as fractions.

$$4\frac{2}{3} \times 5 = \frac{14}{3} \times \frac{5}{1}$$

$$= \frac{4 \times 5}{1 \times 6}$$

Multiply the fractions.

$$= \frac{14 \times 5}{3 \times 1}$$

$$= \frac{20}{6}$$

$$= \frac{70}{3}$$

Change to simplest form.

$$= 3\frac{1}{3}$$

$$= 23\frac{1}{3}$$

Write each answer in simplest form.

	a	b	c	d
1.	$5 \times \frac{2}{3}$	$6 \times \frac{4}{5}$	$\frac{1}{2} \times 9$	$\frac{3}{4} \times 7$
2.	$9 \times \frac{5}{6}$	$\frac{1}{4} \times 6$	$\frac{3}{8} \times 12$	$10 \times \frac{4}{5}$
3.	$2\frac{1}{2} \times 3$	$1\frac{1}{3} \times 5$	$2 \times 3\frac{2}{5}$	$4 \times 4\frac{2}{3}$

NAME _____

Lesson 16 Multiplication

$$2\frac{3}{5} \times 1\frac{1}{6} = \frac{13}{5} \times \frac{7}{6}$$ Change the mixed numerals to fractions.

$$= \frac{13 \times 7}{5 \times 6}$$ Multiply the fractions.

$$= \frac{91}{30}$$

$$= 3\frac{1}{30}$$ Change to simplest form.

Write each answer in simplest form.

	a	*b*	*c*	*d*
1.	$4\frac{2}{3} \times 1\frac{2}{5}$	$3\frac{1}{2} \times 1\frac{1}{6}$	$1\frac{2}{3} \times 2\frac{1}{2}$	$2\frac{2}{3} \times 2\frac{2}{3}$
2.	$2\frac{2}{5} \times 2\frac{1}{4}$	$1\frac{7}{10} \times 2\frac{1}{2}$	$5\frac{1}{3} \times 1\frac{1}{5}$	$2\frac{4}{5} \times 1\frac{1}{7}$
3.	$3\frac{3}{4} \times 2\frac{1}{3}$	$3\frac{2}{5} \times 1\frac{7}{8}$	$4\frac{2}{3} \times 1\frac{1}{8}$	$3\frac{3}{4} \times 3\frac{1}{3}$
4.	$5\frac{1}{6} \times 6\frac{3}{8}$	$2\frac{3}{5} \times 2\frac{1}{2}$	$1\frac{1}{4} \times 1\frac{1}{4}$	$3\frac{1}{8} \times 6\frac{2}{3}$

Problem Solving

Solve. Write each answer in simplest form. Use the space at the right to work each problem.

1. A full box of soap weighs $2\frac{2}{3}$ pounds. How many pounds would $1\frac{1}{3}$ boxes of soap weigh?

   They would weigh _____ pounds.

2. It takes $1\frac{4}{5}$ hours to process 1 ton of ore. How many hours would it take to process $3\frac{1}{3}$ tons of ore?

   It would take _____ hours.

3. Each box of bolts weighs $3\frac{3}{4}$ pounds. How many pounds would $8\frac{1}{2}$ boxes of bolts weigh?

   They would weigh _____ pounds.

4. The boys can walk $3\frac{1}{2}$ miles in 1 hour. At that rate, how many miles could the boys walk in $1\frac{1}{6}$ hours?

   The boys could walk _____ miles.

5. Each bag of apples weighs $4\frac{1}{2}$ pounds. How much would $3\frac{1}{2}$ bags of apples weigh?

   They would weigh _____ pounds.

6. Riding her bicycle, Terry averages $9\frac{1}{2}$ miles per hour. At that speed, how far could she go in $2\frac{2}{3}$ hours?

   She could go _____ miles.

7. In problem 6, suppose Terry averages $9\frac{3}{4}$ miles per hour. How far could she go in $2\frac{2}{3}$ hours?

   She could go _____ miles.

8. A machine can process $2\frac{1}{2}$ tons in 1 hour. How many tons can the machine process in $2\frac{1}{10}$ hours?

   The machine can process _____ tons in $2\frac{1}{10}$ hours.

9. If the machine in problem 8 broke down after $1\frac{1}{2}$ hours, how many tons would have been processed?

   _____ tons would have been processed.

1. _____

2. _____

3. _____

4. _____

5. _____

6. _____

7. _____

8. _____

9. _____

Lesson 17 Addition and Subtraction

Add the numerators.

$$\frac{7}{8}+\frac{5}{8}=\frac{7+5}{8}=\frac{12}{8}=1\frac{1}{2}$$

Use the same denominator.

$$\begin{array}{r}\frac{7}{8}\\+\frac{5}{8}\\\hline\frac{12}{8}=1\frac{1}{2}\end{array}$$

Subtract the numerators.

$$\frac{5}{6}-\frac{1}{6}=\frac{5-1}{6}=\frac{4}{6}=\frac{2}{3}$$

Use the same denominator.

$$\begin{array}{r}\frac{5}{6}\\-\frac{1}{6}\\\hline\frac{4}{6}=\frac{2}{3}\end{array}$$

- - - Change to simplest form. - - -

Write each answer in simplest form.

	a	b	c	d	e
1.	$\frac{1}{5}+\frac{2}{5}$	$\frac{4}{7}+\frac{2}{7}$	$\frac{3}{4}+\frac{2}{4}$	$\frac{5}{6}+\frac{4}{6}$	$\frac{7}{8}+\frac{7}{8}$
2.	$\frac{5}{6}-\frac{4}{6}$	$\frac{7}{8}-\frac{3}{8}$	$\frac{5}{7}-\frac{2}{7}$	$\frac{9}{9}-\frac{4}{9}$	$\frac{5}{8}-\frac{1}{8}$
3.	$\frac{3}{10}+\frac{6}{10}$	$\frac{8}{9}+\frac{4}{9}$	$\frac{3}{8}+\frac{3}{8}$	$\frac{5}{12}+\frac{5}{12}$	$\frac{10}{15}+\frac{14}{15}$
4.	$\frac{11}{12}-\frac{3}{12}$	$\frac{7}{8}-\frac{2}{8}$	$\frac{8}{9}-\frac{5}{9}$	$\frac{9}{10}-\frac{4}{10}$	$\frac{9}{16}-\frac{3}{16}$
5.	$\frac{7}{12}+\frac{8}{12}$	$\frac{5}{9}-\frac{2}{9}$	$\frac{8}{15}+\frac{10}{15}$	$\frac{7}{10}-\frac{3}{10}$	$\frac{6}{14}+\frac{6}{14}$

Lesson 18   Addition and Subtraction

$\dfrac{2}{3}$ $\begin{array}{c}\times 2 \\ \times 2\end{array}$ $=$ $\dfrac{4}{6}$

$+\dfrac{1}{2}$ $\begin{array}{c}\times 3 \\ \times 3\end{array}$ $=$ $+\dfrac{3}{6}$

$\dfrac{7}{6} = 1\dfrac{1}{6}$

The denominators are 3 and 2.
Since $2 \times 3 = 6$, rename each
fraction with a denominator of 6.

Add or subtract the fractions.

Write the answer in simplest form.

$\dfrac{2}{3}$ $\begin{array}{c}\times 2 \\ \times 2\end{array}$ $=$ $\dfrac{4}{6}$

$-\dfrac{1}{2}$ $\begin{array}{c}\times 3 \\ \times 3\end{array}$ $=$ $-\dfrac{3}{6}$

$\dfrac{1}{6}$

Write each answer in simplest form.

	a	b	c	d
1.	$\dfrac{3}{5}$ $+\dfrac{2}{3}$	$\dfrac{5}{6}$ $+\dfrac{1}{5}$	$\dfrac{1}{2}$ $+\dfrac{1}{3}$	$\dfrac{3}{10}$ $+\dfrac{1}{3}$
2.	$\dfrac{2}{3}$ $-\dfrac{1}{4}$	$\dfrac{5}{6}$ $-\dfrac{2}{5}$	$\dfrac{7}{8}$ $-\dfrac{2}{3}$	$\dfrac{3}{4}$ $-\dfrac{1}{3}$
3.	$\dfrac{7}{8}$ $+\dfrac{1}{3}$	$\dfrac{7}{8}$ $-\dfrac{1}{3}$	$\dfrac{2}{5}$ $+\dfrac{3}{4}$	$\dfrac{1}{2}$ $-\dfrac{1}{3}$
4.	$\dfrac{1}{3}$ $+\dfrac{3}{4}$	$\dfrac{3}{5}$ $-\dfrac{1}{3}$	$\dfrac{1}{2}$ $+\dfrac{4}{5}$	$\dfrac{3}{4}$ $-\dfrac{2}{3}$

Lesson 19 Addition

$3\dfrac{1}{2} \longrightarrow 3\dfrac{4}{8}$

$+1\dfrac{1}{8} \longrightarrow +1\dfrac{1}{8}$

$\quad\qquad\qquad 4\dfrac{5}{8}$

Rename the numbers so the fractions have the same denominator.
Add the fractions.
Add the whole numbers.

Change to simplest form.

$1\dfrac{1}{2} \longrightarrow 1\dfrac{6}{12}$

$3\dfrac{3}{4} \longrightarrow 3\dfrac{9}{12}$

$+\dfrac{2}{3} \longrightarrow +\dfrac{8}{12}$

$4\dfrac{23}{12} = 5\dfrac{11}{12}$

Write each answer in simplest form.

	a	b	c	d
1.	$3\dfrac{1}{4}$ $+2\dfrac{4}{5}$	$3\dfrac{1}{6}$ $+\dfrac{3}{4}$	$5\dfrac{1}{2}$ $+1\dfrac{5}{8}$	$3\dfrac{11}{12}$ $+\dfrac{5}{6}$
2.	$9\dfrac{7}{8}$ $+\dfrac{3}{4}$	$7\dfrac{2}{5}$ $+4\dfrac{3}{10}$	$\dfrac{3}{5}$ $+2\dfrac{5}{6}$	$\dfrac{9}{10}$ $+3\dfrac{5}{6}$
3.	$6\dfrac{2}{3}$ $1\dfrac{3}{4}$ $+\dfrac{1}{6}$	$2\dfrac{1}{5}$ $2\dfrac{1}{4}$ $+1\dfrac{1}{2}$	$3\dfrac{1}{3}$ $\dfrac{5}{6}$ $+3\dfrac{7}{12}$	$\dfrac{1}{2}$ $5\dfrac{1}{5}$ $+1\dfrac{3}{10}$
4.	$\dfrac{3}{5}$ $1\dfrac{2}{3}$ $+2\dfrac{1}{2}$	$3\dfrac{5}{8}$ $2\dfrac{1}{6}$ $+\dfrac{5}{12}$	$\dfrac{1}{4}$ $1\dfrac{1}{2}$ $+4\dfrac{7}{8}$	$2\dfrac{2}{3}$ $2\dfrac{1}{2}$ $+3\dfrac{2}{5}$

Lesson 20 Subtraction

$3\frac{2}{3} \longrightarrow 3\frac{4}{6}$

$-1\frac{1}{6} \longrightarrow -1\frac{1}{6}$

$\phantom{-1\frac{1}{6} \longrightarrow} 2\frac{3}{6} = 2\frac{1}{2}$

Rename the numbers so the fractions have the same denominator.
Subtract the fractions.
Subtract the whole numbers.
Change to simplest form.

$3 \longrightarrow 2\frac{4}{4}$

$-\frac{1}{4} \longrightarrow -\frac{1}{4}$

$\phantom{-\frac{1}{4} \longrightarrow} 2\frac{3}{4}$

$3 = 2 + 1$
$= 2 + \frac{4}{4}$
$= 2\frac{4}{4}$

Write each answer in simplest form.

	a	*b*	*c*	*d*
1.	7 $-\frac{3}{4}$	4 $-\frac{1}{2}$	5 $-\frac{2}{3}$	8 $-\frac{1}{8}$
2.	$3\frac{4}{5}$ $-1\frac{1}{2}$	$5\frac{2}{3}$ $-3\frac{4}{9}$	$4\frac{5}{6}$ $-1\frac{1}{2}$	$5\frac{9}{10}$ $-3\frac{2}{5}$
3.	5 $-\frac{3}{5}$	$6\frac{3}{4}$ $-5\frac{1}{8}$	$2\frac{2}{3}$ $-1\frac{1}{2}$	10 $-2\frac{3}{10}$
4.	$10\frac{5}{6}$ $-7\frac{5}{12}$	8 $-\frac{5}{8}$	$9\frac{5}{6}$ $-2\frac{1}{3}$	6 $-\frac{9}{10}$

Problem Solving

Solve. Write each answer in simplest form. Use the space at the right to work each problem.

1. A CD has been playing for $\frac{1}{3}$ hour. The CD still has $\frac{5}{12}$ hour to play. What is the total length of time the CD can play?

   The CD can play _____ hour.

2. It rained $\frac{3}{4}$ inch yesterday and $\frac{3}{10}$ inch today. How much more did it rain yesterday?

   It rained _____ inch more yesterday.

3. Matthew spent $\frac{1}{2}$ hour doing his history homework and $\frac{3}{4}$ hour doing his science homework. How much time did he spend doing homework?

   He spent _____ hours doing homework.

4. Rob has a board that is $\frac{1}{8}$ inch too wide. The board is $\frac{3}{4}$ inch wide. What width board does Rob need?

   Rob needs a board _____ inch wide.

5. Maranda read $\frac{3}{5}$ hour in the morning and $\frac{1}{2}$ hour in the afternoon. How many hours did she read in the morning and afternoon?

   She read _____ hours.

6. In problem 5, how much longer did she read in the morning than in the afternoon?

   She read _____ hour longer in the morning.

7. John has two boxes. One weighs $\frac{3}{10}$ pound and the other weighs $\frac{7}{8}$ pound. What is the combined weight of both boxes?

   The combined weight is _____ pounds.

8. In problem 7, how much more does the heavier box weigh?

   The heavier box weighs _____ pound more.

| 1. |
| 2. |
| 3. |
| 4. |
| 5. |
| 6. |
| 7. |
| 8. |

Lesson 21 Reciprocals

The product of any number and its **reciprocal** is 1.

reciprocals

$$\frac{2}{3} \times \frac{3}{2} = \frac{2 \times 3}{3 \times 2} = \frac{6}{6} = 1$$

The reciprocal of $\frac{2}{3}$ is $\frac{3}{2}$.

The reciprocal of $\frac{3}{2}$ is $\frac{2}{3}$.

reciprocals

$$\frac{1}{2} \times \frac{2}{1} = \frac{1 \times 2}{2 \times 1} = \frac{2}{2} = 1$$

The reciprocal of $\frac{1}{2}$ is $\frac{2}{1}$ or 2 .

The reciprocal of 2 is $\frac{1}{2}$.

Write the reciprocal of each of the following.

	a	b	c	d	e	f
1.	$\frac{3}{5}$ ___	$\frac{7}{8}$ ___	$\frac{4}{5}$ ___	$\frac{5}{7}$ ___	$\frac{4}{9}$ ___	$\frac{6}{7}$ ___
2.	$\frac{5}{3}$ ___	$\frac{8}{7}$ ___	$\frac{5}{4}$ ___	$\frac{7}{5}$ ___	$\frac{9}{4}$ ___	$\frac{7}{6}$ ___
3.	$\frac{1}{8}$ ___	$\frac{1}{3}$ ___	$\frac{1}{4}$ ___	$\frac{1}{9}$ ___	$\frac{1}{16}$ ___	$\frac{1}{14}$ ___
4.	$\frac{8}{1}$ ___	$\frac{3}{1}$ ___	$\frac{4}{1}$ ___	$\frac{9}{1}$ ___	$\frac{16}{1}$ ___	$\frac{14}{1}$ ___
5.	8 ___	3 ___	4 ___	9 ___	16 ___	14 ___
6.	$\frac{8}{5}$ ___	6 ___	$\frac{2}{3}$ ___	$\frac{11}{6}$ ___	$\frac{7}{4}$ ___	12 ___
7.	15 ___	$\frac{10}{9}$ ___	$\frac{12}{11}$ ___	17 ___	$\frac{8}{9}$ ___	$\frac{17}{2}$ ___
8.	$\frac{15}{8}$ ___	$\frac{5}{12}$ ___	11 ___	$\frac{7}{11}$ ___	$\frac{1}{11}$ ___	$\frac{17}{3}$ ___
9.	$\frac{10}{1}$ ___	13 ___	$\frac{1}{17}$ ___	$\frac{5}{11}$ ___	$\frac{9}{7}$ ___	5 ___
10.	$\frac{5}{8}$ ___	$\frac{1}{6}$ ___	7 ___	$\frac{12}{7}$ ___	2 ___	$\frac{2}{5}$ ___

Lesson 22 Division

$$15 \div \frac{3}{4} = \frac{15}{1} \times \frac{4}{3}$$

$$= \frac{15 \times 4}{1 \times 3}$$

$$= \frac{60}{3}$$

$$= 20$$

To divide by a fraction, multiply by its reciprocal.

Multiply the fractions.

Write the answer in simplest form.

$$10 \div \frac{6}{7} = \frac{10}{1} \times \frac{7}{6}$$

$$= \frac{10 \times 7}{1 \times 6}$$

$$= \frac{70}{6}$$

$$= 11\frac{2}{3}$$

Write each answer in simplest form.

	a	*b*	*c*	*d*
1.	$10 \div \frac{1}{3}$	$8 \div \frac{1}{2}$	$7 \div \frac{1}{4}$	$6 \div \frac{1}{5}$
2.	$14 \div \frac{2}{7}$	$15 \div \frac{2}{5}$	$16 \div \frac{3}{8}$	$18 \div \frac{5}{9}$
3.	$18 \div \frac{1}{3}$	$14 \div \frac{7}{8}$	$17 \div \frac{1}{2}$	$12 \div \frac{3}{4}$

Lesson 23   Division

Multiply by
the reciprocal.

$$\frac{1}{4} \div \frac{1}{3} = \frac{1}{4} \times \frac{3}{1}$$

$$= \frac{1 \times 3}{4 \times 1}$$

$$= \frac{3}{4}$$

Multiply by
the reciprocal.

$$\frac{3}{4} \div \frac{1}{2} = \frac{3}{4} \times \frac{2}{1}$$

$$= \frac{3 \times 2}{4 \times 1}$$

$$= \frac{6}{4}$$ Write the
answer in
simplest form.

$$= 1\frac{2}{4}$$

$$= 1\frac{1}{2}$$

Write each answer in simplest form.

	a	b	c	d
1.	$\frac{1}{5} \div \frac{1}{2}$	$\frac{1}{3} \div \frac{1}{2}$	$\frac{1}{8} \div \frac{1}{4}$	$\frac{1}{9} \div \frac{1}{6}$
2.	$\frac{3}{5} \div \frac{1}{2}$	$\frac{4}{7} \div \frac{2}{3}$	$\frac{4}{5} \div \frac{1}{10}$	$\frac{5}{6} \div \frac{2}{3}$
3.	$\frac{4}{5} \div \frac{2}{5}$	$\frac{3}{8} \div \frac{3}{4}$	$\frac{4}{9} \div \frac{1}{5}$	$\frac{7}{8} \div \frac{7}{10}$

Problem Solving

Solve. Write each answer in simplest form. Use the space at the right to work each problem.

1. How many $\frac{1}{6}$-hour sessions are there in $\frac{1}{2}$ hour?

   There are _____ sessions.

2. Erika has a ribbon $\frac{3}{4}$ yard long. How many $\frac{1}{4}$-yard pieces can she get from her ribbon?

   She can get _____ pieces.

3. In problem 2, how many $\frac{1}{8}$-yard pieces can Erika get from her ribbon?

   She can get _____ pieces.

4. A machine uses gas at the rate of $\frac{1}{5}$ gallon an hour. So far $\frac{9}{10}$ gallon has been used. How many hours has the machine operated?

   The machine has operated _____ hours.

5. Suppose the machine in problem 4 has used $\frac{4}{5}$ gallon of gas. How many hours did the machine operate?

   The machine operated _____ hours.

6. Three-eighths pound of nuts is put in each bag. How many bags can be filled with $\frac{3}{4}$ pound of nuts?

   _____ bags can be filled.

7. Jason walked $\frac{5}{6}$ hour. He walked at the rate of 1 mile every $\frac{1}{6}$ hour. How many miles did he walk?

   He walked _____ miles.

8. Suppose in problem 7 Jason walked 1 mile every $\frac{5}{12}$ hour. How many miles did he walk?

   He walked _____ miles.

9. A bell rings every $\frac{1}{6}$ hour. Assume it just rang. How many times will it ring in the next $\frac{2}{3}$ hour?

   It will ring _____ times.

1.
2.
3.
4.
5.
6.
7.
8.
9.

Lesson 24 Division

$$2\frac{1}{5} \div 4 = \frac{11}{5} \div 4$$

Change the mixed numerals to fractions.

$$= \frac{11}{5} \times \frac{1}{4}$$

To divide, multiply by the reciprocal.

$$= \frac{11}{20}$$

Multiply the fractions.

Write the answer in simplest form.

$$3\frac{1}{2} \div 1\frac{1}{2} = \frac{7}{2} \div \frac{3}{2}$$

$$= \frac{7}{2} \times \frac{2}{3}$$

$$= \frac{14}{6}$$

$$= 2\frac{1}{3}$$

Write each answer in simplest form.

	a	b	c	d
1.	$2\frac{1}{2} \div 3$	$1\frac{2}{5} \div 3$	$4 \div 1\frac{1}{3}$	$6 \div 1\frac{1}{3}$
2.	$1\frac{2}{7} \div 2\frac{1}{2}$	$1\frac{1}{5} \div 2\frac{2}{3}$	$4\frac{1}{2} \div 1\frac{1}{5}$	$1\frac{4}{5} \div 1\frac{1}{5}$
3.	$1\frac{4}{5} \div \frac{2}{7}$	$\frac{1}{6} \div 1\frac{1}{2}$	$3\frac{3}{5} \div 10$	$1\frac{1}{3} \div 2\frac{1}{2}$

Lesson 25 Tenths

Numerals like 0.4, 4.1, and 5.4 are called **decimals.**

$\frac{1}{10} = 0.1$ 0.1 is read "one tenth."

$0.4 = \frac{4}{10}$ $\frac{3}{10} = 0.3$

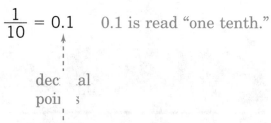

dec al
poi 3

$4\frac{1}{10} = 4$ 4.1 is read "four and one tenth." $5.4 = 5\frac{4}{10}$ $2\frac{3}{10} = 2.3$

Change each fraction or mixed numeral to a decimal.

$\qquad a \qquad\qquad b \qquad\qquad c \qquad\qquad d$

1. $\frac{6}{10} =$ _____ $\frac{2}{10} =$ _____ $\frac{8}{10} =$ _____ $\frac{5}{10} =$ _____

2. $4\frac{7}{10} =$ _____ $5\frac{9}{10} =$ _____ $18\frac{2}{10} =$ _____ $423\frac{6}{10} =$ _____

Change each decimal to a fraction or mixed numeral.

3. 0.7 = _____   0.3 = _____   0.1 = _____   0.9 = _____

4. 4.9 = _____   12.7 = _____   15.1 = _____   217.3 = _____

Write a decimal for each of the following.

$\qquad a \qquad\qquad\qquad\qquad\qquad\qquad b$

5. eight tenths _____   three and seven tenths _____

6. four tenths _____   twenty-five and eight tenths _____

7. five tenths _____   one hundred and six tenths _____

Write each decimal in words.

8. 0.9 _____

9. 3.7 _____

10. 21.2 _____

NAME _____

Lesson 26   Hundredths

$\frac{1}{100} = 0.01$ 0.01 is read "one hundredth."

$0.15 = \frac{15}{100}$ $\frac{9}{100} = 0.09$

$3\frac{12}{100} = 3.12$ 3.12 is read
"three and twelve hundredths." $2.07 = 2\frac{7}{100}$ $1\frac{14}{100} = 1.14$

Change each fraction or mixed numeral to a decimal naming hundredths.

	a	b	c
1.	$\frac{8}{100} =$ ___	$\frac{16}{100} =$ ___	$\frac{5}{100} =$ ___
2.	$1\frac{36}{100} =$ ___	$8\frac{6}{100} =$ ___	$9\frac{12}{100} =$ ___
3.	$12\frac{45}{100} =$ ___	$43\frac{67}{100} =$ ___	$26\frac{4}{100} =$ ___
4.	$142\frac{8}{100} =$ ___	$436\frac{42}{100} =$ ___	$389\frac{89}{100} =$ ___

Change each decimal to a fraction or mixed numeral.

5.   0.17 = ___   0.03 = ___   0.41 = ___

6.   5.19 = ___   6.47 = ___   5.01 = ___

7.   21.07 = ___   23.99 = ___   44.89 = ___

8. 142.33 = ___   483.03 = ___   185.63 = ___

Write a decimal for each of the following.

a   b

9. eight hundredths ___   six and twenty-three hundredths ___

10. ninety-five hundredths ___   fourteen and sixty hundredths ___

11. forty-eight hundredths ___   four and forty-four hundredths ___

Lesson 27   Thousandths, Ten-Thousandths

$$\frac{1}{1000} = 0.001 \longleftarrow \text{one thousandth} \qquad \frac{1}{10000} = 0.0001 \longleftarrow \text{one ten-thousandth}$$

$$2\frac{12}{1000} = 2.012 \longleftarrow \text{two and twelve} \qquad 1\frac{35}{10000} = 1.0035 \longleftarrow \text{one and thirty-five}$$
$$\text{thousandths} \qquad\qquad\qquad \text{ten-thousandths}$$

Write each fraction or mixed numeral as a decimal.

	a	*b*	*c*
1.	$\frac{8}{1000} =$ _____	$\frac{17}{1000} =$ _____	$\frac{54}{10000} =$ _____
2.	$\frac{125}{10000} =$ _____	$\frac{430}{1000} =$ _____	$\frac{306}{10000} =$ _____
3.	$4\frac{4}{1000} =$ _____	$3\frac{41}{10000} =$ _____	$6\frac{183}{1000} =$ _____
4.	$35\frac{78}{10000} =$ _____	$42\frac{19}{1000} =$ _____	$196\frac{6}{1000} =$ _____

Write each decimal as a fraction or as a mixed numeral.

	a	*b*	*c*
5.	$0.009 =$ _____	$0.0019 =$ _____	$0.0003 =$ _____
6.	$0.123 =$ _____	$0.0441 =$ _____	$0.219 =$ _____
7.	$4.011 =$ _____	$2.1011 =$ _____	$6.0014 =$ _____
8.	$36.037 =$ _____	$3.433 =$ _____	$100.0001 =$ _____

Write a decimal for each of the following.

	a		*b*	
9.	fifty-three thousandths	_____	ten and nine ten-thousandths	_____
10.	eleven ten-thousandths	_____	twelve and eighteen thousandths	_____
11.	sixty-five thousandths	_____	twelve and one thousandth	_____

Lesson 28   Fractions to Decimals

Change $\frac{1}{2}$ to tenths.

$$\frac{1}{2} = \frac{1}{2} \times \frac{5}{5}$$
$$= \frac{5}{10}$$
$$= 0.5$$

Change $\frac{1}{2}$ to hundredths.

$$\frac{1}{2} = \frac{1}{2} \times \frac{50}{50}$$
$$= \frac{50}{100}$$
$$= 0.50$$

Change $\frac{1}{2}$ to thousandths.

$$\frac{1}{2} = \frac{1}{2} \times \frac{500}{500}$$
$$= \frac{500}{1000}$$
$$= 0.500$$

Change $\frac{3}{4}$ to hundredths.

$$\frac{3}{4} = \frac{3}{4} \times \frac{25}{25}$$
$$= \frac{75}{100}$$
$$= \underline{.75}$$

Change $3\frac{48}{250}$ to thousandths.

$$3\frac{48}{250} = 3 + \frac{48}{250}$$
$$= 3 + \left(\frac{48}{250} \times \frac{4}{4}\right)$$
$$= 3 + \frac{192}{1000}$$
$$= 3\frac{192}{1000}$$
$$= \underline{3.192}$$

Change each of the following to a decimal as indicated.

a	*b*	*c*

1. Change $\frac{3}{5}$ to tenths.   Change $\frac{3}{5}$ to hundredths.   Change $\frac{3}{5}$ to thousandths.

2. Change $3\frac{1}{2}$ to tenths.   Change $\frac{7}{25}$ to hundredths.   Change $2\frac{19}{100}$ to thousandths.

3. Change $2\frac{4}{5}$ to tenths.   Change $\frac{7}{20}$ to hundredths.   Change $\frac{7}{125}$ to thousandths.

4. Change $2\frac{1}{5}$ to tenths.   Change $\frac{19}{50}$ to hundredths.   Change $\frac{88}{250}$ to thousandths.

Lesson 29   Decimals to Fractions

$0.7 = \frac{7}{10}$ $\qquad$ $0.6 = \frac{6}{10}$ or $\frac{3}{5}$ $\qquad$ $4.2 = 4\frac{2}{10}$ or $4\frac{1}{5}$

$0.19 = \frac{19}{100}$ $\qquad$ $0.14 = \frac{14}{100}$ or $\frac{7}{50}$ $\qquad$ $3.01 = 3\frac{1}{100}$

$0.051 = \dfrac{51}{1000}$ $\qquad$ $0.114 = \frac{114}{1000}$ or $\dfrac{57}{500}$ $\qquad$ $5.006 = 5\frac{6}{1000}$ or $5\dfrac{3}{500}$

Change each decimal to a fraction or mixed numeral in simplest form.

	a	b	c	d
1.	0.3	0.1	0.4	0.5
2.	2.7	3.3	7.2	5.8
3.	0.17	0.03	0.15	0.80
4.	5.07	8.43	4.05	2.44
5.	0.003	0.017	0.125	0.045
6.	3.121	2.987	4.250	3.008
7.	4.35	0.7	6.200	1.007
8.	2.6	3.24	0.250	3.5
9.	5.125	0.9	2.4	0.04
10.	0.01	0.051	0.8	2.19

Lesson 30 Addition

When adding decimals, line up the decimal points.
Add decimals like you add whole numbers.

$$
\begin{array}{r} 0.6 \\ +0.7 \\ \hline 1.3 \end{array}
\qquad
\begin{array}{r} \overset{1}{3.5}\,6 \\ 0.0\,3 \\ +4.2\,4 \\ \hline 7.8\,3 \end{array}
\qquad
\begin{array}{r} 3.0\,\overset{1}{1}\,8 \\ 0.1\,4\,2 \\ +1\,4.0\,0\,9 \\ \hline 1\,7.1\,6\,9 \end{array}
$$

Place the decimal point in the answer.

Add.

	a	*b*	*c*	*d*	*e*
1.	$\begin{array}{r}0.4\\+0.5\\\hline\end{array}$	$\begin{array}{r}0.9\\+0.8\\\hline\end{array}$	$\begin{array}{r}3.4\\+9.2\\\hline\end{array}$	$\begin{array}{r}1\,9.3\\+1\,2.8\\\hline\end{array}$	$\begin{array}{r}4\,5.6\\+\ 6.8\\\hline\end{array}$
2.	$\begin{array}{r}0.\,4\,2\\+0.\,3\,5\\\hline\end{array}$	$\begin{array}{r}0.7\,6\\+0.4\,8\\\hline\end{array}$	$\begin{array}{r}3.3\,2\\+4.6\,2\\\hline\end{array}$	$\begin{array}{r}2\,4.4\,5\\+7\,2.3\,6\\\hline\end{array}$	$\begin{array}{r}5\,8.9\,2\\+3.2\,9\\\hline\end{array}$
3.	$\begin{array}{r}0.0\,1\,4\\+0.2\,3\,1\\\hline\end{array}$	$\begin{array}{r}0.4\,5\,6\\+0.8\,7\,6\\\hline\end{array}$	$\begin{array}{r}2.0\,1\,4\\+2.3\,2\,5\\\hline\end{array}$	$\begin{array}{r}3.4\,5\,7\\+2.3\,5\,6\\\hline\end{array}$	$\begin{array}{r}4\,1.2\,1\,6\\+2.0\,0\,7\\\hline\end{array}$
4.	$\begin{array}{r}0.5\\0.6\\+0.7\\\hline\end{array}$	$\begin{array}{r}1.9\\2.2\\+3.4\\\hline\end{array}$	$\begin{array}{r}3.4\\1.7\\+4.8\\\hline\end{array}$	$\begin{array}{r}4\,2.3\\1.6\\+2.9\\\hline\end{array}$	$\begin{array}{r}3.4\\0.8\\+4.2\\\hline\end{array}$
5.	$\begin{array}{r}0.3\,3\\0.2\,6\\+0.4\,1\\\hline\end{array}$	$\begin{array}{r}\$0.4\,3\\0.5\,4\\+0.0\,7\\\hline\end{array}$	$\begin{array}{r}3.3\,5\\1.0\,8\\+6.1\,1\\\hline\end{array}$	$\begin{array}{r}\$2\,4.2\,9\\1\,2.2\,9\\+5.3\,1\\\hline\end{array}$	$\begin{array}{r}\$3\,4.0\,5\\2.0\,6\\+1.0\,8\\\hline\end{array}$
6.	$\begin{array}{r}0.0\,1\,2\\0.3\,0\,4\\+0.4\,0\,5\\\hline\end{array}$	$\begin{array}{r}0.4\,2\,3\\0.0\,5\,6\\+0.2\,1\,7\\\hline\end{array}$	$\begin{array}{r}3.0\,5\,6\\1.4\,5\,2\\+6.1\,1\,2\\\hline\end{array}$	$\begin{array}{r}4.0\,0\,8\\2.3\,0\,9\\+0.0\,1\,2\\\hline\end{array}$	$\begin{array}{r}3\,5.1\,5\,7\\0.4\,4\,8\\+2.5\,0\,9\\\hline\end{array}$

Lesson 31   Addition

You may write these 0's
if they help you add.

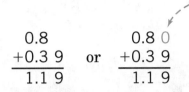

0.8		0.8 0			4.2		4.2 0 0
+0.3 9	or	+0.3 9			3.0 1 8	or	3.0 1 8
1.1 9		1.1 9			+0.8 2		+0.8 2 0
					8.0 3 8		8.0 3 8

Add. If necessary, use 0's as shown in the examples.

	a	*b*	*c*	*d*	*e*
1.	0.9 +0.4 2	0.8 3 +0.4	0.6 +0.4 0 1	0.7 2 +0.4 2 3	0.6 4 5 +0.2
2.	2.7 5 +3.3 0 8	5.5 4 +7.6	3.8 +0.3 1 6	0.2 9 +8.0 4 3	2 9.5 + 4.9 3
3.	0.4 2 0.8 +0.0 1 8	0.3 1 0.2 +0.4 5	0.7 6 0.8 2 +0.9	0.4 3 1 0.2 +0.4 5	0.5 0.3 1 6 +0.0 9 9
4.	3.1 8 2 1.3 4 +2.6	4.7 2 5.8 +6.3 1 7	7.4 2 6 3.3 1 8 +0.2	0.7 3 1 8.4 5 +2.2 8	0.3 0.3 8 4 +9.4 2

Complete the following.

	a	*b*

5. 0.8 + 0.91 = _____   0.4 + 0.016 + 0.75 = _____

6. 0.58 + 0.114 = _____   0.32 + 0.42 + 0.113 = _____

7. 0.9 + 0.301 = _____   4.8 + 3.21 + 0.014 = _____

8. 2.4 + 0.31 = _____   5.24 + 0.016 + 21.3 = _____

Lesson 32   Subtraction

> When subtracting decimals, line up the decimal points. Subtract decimals like you subtract whole numbers.

9.5	$\overset{3\ 13}{4.\cancel{3}}$	$\overset{0\ 14}{0.1\ \cancel{4}}$	$\overset{3\ 12}{4\ \cancel{2}.7}\ \overset{4\ 13}{\cancel{5}\ \cancel{3}}$
−2.3	−1.6	−0.0 8	−5.3 2 7
7.2	2.7	0.0 6	3 7.4 2 6

Place the decimal point in the answer.

Subtract.

	a	*b*	*c*	*d*	*e*
1.	0.7 −0.3	0.9 −0.2	0.6 −0.2	0.9 −0.1	0.8 −0.5
2.	0.4 2 −0.3 1	0.5 6 −0.2 3	0.0 7 −0.0 2	0.8 5 −0.3 7	$0.5 2 −0.3 7
3.	0.3 4 5 −0.2 3 4	0.5 4 8 −0.2 5 9	0.8 1 5 −0.6 0 7	0.8 2 8 −0.3 8 9	0.7 5 4 −0.3 7 5
4.	4.6 −3.2	7.4 −2.8	8.6 −3.7	5.6 −0.7	1 9.2 −0.9
5.	4.3 6 −1.2 3	$6.5 5 −2.7 3	4.0 8 −0.3 9	$1 5.3 2 −2.6 7	$ 4.0 9 −0.3 2
6.	4.2 1 3 −2.0 0 1	3.6 2 4 −1.4 1 5	4.3 0 7 −1.4 9 5	26.3 4 5 −2.5 4 3	15.1 0 8 −3.9 1 2
7.	1 5.3 −4.9	6.2 3 −3.7 5	14.2 1 −7.0 8	3.0 0 2 −1.0 4 7	19.8 0 1 −7.4 1 3

Lesson 33 Subtraction

```
  5 14              5 14                                            3 10
6.4 3 2           6.4 3 2                          6.4        6.4 0  ←— Write this
−1.7      or    −1.7 0 0  ←—Write these        −1.2 3    →  −1.2 3     0 to help
───────         ─────────    0's if they        ───────     ───────   you subtract.
4.7 3 2           4.7 3 2     help you.                       5.1 7
```

Subtract.

	a	*b*	*c*	*d*	*e*
1.	0.7 2 −0.2	3.5 6 −1.4	5.3 8 −2.7	4.3 1 6 −1.1	2.1 4 6 −1.5
2.	0.5 2 3 −0.4 1	0.683 −0.39	5.4 2 1 −0.5 6	3.0 1 8 −0.2 7	4.0 1 2 −3.0 3
3.	0.8 −0.3 5	0.5 −0.2 6	6.3 −1.1 2	7.4 −2.7 5	1 4.3 −6.7 2
4.	0.9 −0.3 0 9	0.3 −0.1 7 5	4.4 −2.3 5 6	6.3 −3.4 3 2	1 8.2 −7.5 1 4
5.	0.7 5 −0.3 1 4	0.3 6 −0.2 7 5	5.7 2 −1.3 1 2	4.3 8 −0.5 9 2	1 6.9 2 −6.3 8 4
6.	3 4.2 6 5 −2.1 8	42.1 6 −3.2 3 5	4 2.2 −3.1 6 4	2 6.3 −2.4 5	3.1 0 6 −2.0 3
7.	4 3.7 −6.1 8	3 9 4.6 −7 5.8 1	5.2 1 6 −4.1 9	8 2.4 5 −3.7 8 3	9 2.4 0 5 −3.0 0 8

Problem Solving

Today's Work Report		
Ms. Williams	14.7 units	1.2 hours
Mr. Karns	8.4 units	0.9 hour
Mr. Anders	13.5 units	1.4 hours

The manufacturing director uses her computer to find out how many units her workers are producing. Use the information above to solve each problem. Use the space at the right to work each problem.

1. How many more units did Ms. Williams make than Mr. Anders?

   Ms. Williams made _____ more units.

2. Who made the most units? Who made the fewest units? What is the difference between the most and the fewest units made?

   _____ made the most units.

   _____ made the fewest units.

   The difference is _____ units.

3. How many units did the three workers make in all?

   The three workers made _____ units.

4. How long did the three workers work on the units in all?

   The three workers worked _____ hours.

1.

2.

3.

4.

44

Lesson 34   Multiplication

number of digits to the right of the
decimal point

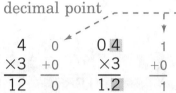 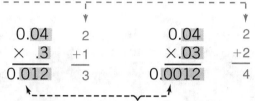

4 0	0.4 1	0.04 2	0.04 2	0.04 2
×3 +0	×3 +0	× 3 +0	× .3 +1	×.03 +2
12 0	1.2 1	0.12 2	0.012 3	0.0012 4

Write in as many 0's as needed to
place the decimal point correctly.

Multiply.

	a	b	c	d	e
1.	2 ×3	0.2 ×3	0.0 2 ×3	0.0 0 2 ×3	2 ×0.3
2.	8 ×6	0.8 ×6	0.0 8 ×6	0.0 0 8 ×6	0.0 6 ×8
3.	5 ×3	0.5 ×3	0.0 5 ×3	0.0 0 5 ×3	0.0 0 3 ×5
4.	3 ×4	0.3 ×0.4	0.0 3 ×0.4	0. 0 4 ×0.3	0.0 3 ×0.0 4
5.	6 ×7	0.6 ×0.7	0.0 6 ×0.7	0.0 7 ×0.6	0.0 6 ×0.0 7
6.	9 ×8	0.9 ×0.8	0.0 9 ×0.8	0.0 8 ×0.9	0.0 9 ×0.0 8

Lesson 35 Multiplication

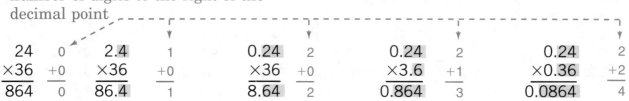

number of digits to the right of the
decimal point

24	0	2.4	1	0.24	2	0.24	2	0.24	2
×36	+0	×36	+0	×36	+0	×3.6	+1	×0.36	+2
864	0	86.4	1	8.64	2	0.864	3	0.0864	4

Use the completed multiplication to find each product.

		a	*b*	*c*	*d*
1.	32 ×14 448	3.2 ×1 4	0.3 2 ×1 4	0.3 2 ×1.4	0.3 2 ×0.1 4
2.	27 ×48 1,296	2.7 ×4 8	0.2 7 ×4 8	0.2 7 ×4.8	0.2 7 ×0.4 8
3.	26 ×34 884	0.2 6 ×3 4	0.2 6 ×3.4	0.2 6 ×0.3 4	2.6 ×3 4
4.	74 ×26 1,924	0.7 4 ×2.6	7.4 ×2 6	0.7 4 ×2 6	0.7 4 ×0.2 6
5.	25 ×3 75	2 5 ×0.3	2.5 ×0.0 3	2 5 ×0.03	0.2 5 ×0.0 3
6.	12 ×4 48	1.2 ×0.4	0.1 2 ×4	0.1 2 ×0.4	0.1 2 ×0.0 4
7.	73 ×3 219	7 3 ×0.0 3	0.7 3 ×0.0 3	7.3 ×0.3	0.7 3 ×0.3

Lesson 36 Multiplication

2.51	2.51	2.51
×10	×100	×1000
25.10	251.00	2510.00
or	or	or
25.1	251	2,510

Shortcut

2.51 × 10 = 2 5.1

2.51 × 100 = 2 51

2.51 × 1000 = 2 510

0.085	0.085	0.085
×10	×100	×1000
0.850	8.500	85.000
or	or	or
0.85	8.5	85

0.085 × 10 = 0.85

0.085 × 100 = 08.5

0.085 × 1000 = 085

Multiply.

	a	*b*	*c*	*d*	*e*
1.	5.6 4 2 ×1 0	5.6 4 2 ×1 0 0	5.6 4 2 ×1 0 0 0	5 6.4 2 ×1 0 0	0.5 6 4 2 ×1 0
2.	0.1 0 6 4 ×1 0	0.1 0 6 4 ×1 0 0	0.1 0 6 4 ×1 0 0 0	0.0 1 0 6 ×1 0	1.0 6 4 ×1 0 0 0
3.	0.2 3 ×1 0	0.2 3 ×1 0 0	0.2 3 ×1 0 0 0	0.0 2 3 ×1 0	0.0 0 2 3 ×1 0 0
4.	0.0 0 8 ×1 0	0.0 0 8 ×1 0 0	0.0 0 8 ×1 0 0 0	0.0 8 ×1 0 0	0.0 8 ×1 0 0 0
5.	1.5 ×1 0	1.5 ×1 0 0	1.5 ×1 0 0 0	1 5 ×1 0 0	0.1 5 ×1 0

NAME _____

Lesson 37　Division

Place a decimal point in the quotient directly
above the decimal point in the dividend. Then
divide as if both numbers were whole numbers.

```
      17              1.7             0.17            0.017
6) 102          6) 10.2         6) 1.02         6) 0.102
   60              60              60              60
   42              42              42              42
   42              42              42              42
    0               0               0               0
```

Divide.

	a	*b*	*c*	*d*	*e*

1. 4) 2 9 2 　　4) 2 9.2 　　4) 2.9 2 　　4) 0. 2 9 2 　　4) 0.0 2 9 2

2. 3) 5.6 1 　　8) 0.0 2 1 6 　　7) 0.2 3 1 　　4) 4.6 4 　　6) 2 5.2

3. 7) 2 4.5 　　8) 0.3 3 6 　　6) 0.0 1 6 2 　　4) 2 4.4 　　3) 1.6 8

48

Lesson 38 Division

> Multiply the divisor and the dividend by 10, by 100, or by 1000 so the new divisor is a whole number.

$$0.8 \overline{)\ 32} \longrightarrow 0.8 \overline{)\ 32.0} \longrightarrow 8 \overline{)\ 320}$$

Multiply by 10.

```
    40
8) 320
   320
     0
```

$$0.004 \overline{)\ 26} \longrightarrow 0.004 \overline{)\ 26.000} \longrightarrow 4 \overline{)\ 26000}$$

Multiply by 1000.

```
   6,500
4) 26000
   24000
    2000
    2000
       0
```

$$0.05 \overline{)\ 45} \longrightarrow 0.05 \overline{)\ 45.00} \longrightarrow 5 \overline{)\ 4500}$$

Multiply by 100.

```
    900
5) 4500
   4500
      0
```

Divide.

	a	b	c	d
1.	$0.4 \overline{)\ 7\ 2}$	$0.3 \overline{)\ 8\ 1}$	$0.7 \overline{)\ 3\ 5\ 7}$	$0.3 \overline{)\ 1\ 1\ 1}$
2.	$0.03 \overline{)\ 5\ 4}$	$0.04 \overline{)\ 9\ 6}$	$0.05 \overline{)\ 8\ 5}$	$0.08 \overline{)\ 2\ 9\ 6}$
3.	$0.002 \overline{)\ 6}$	$0.004 \overline{)\ 1\ 2}$	$0.006 \overline{)\ 2\ 4}$	$0.005 \overline{)\ 1\ 5\ 5}$

Lesson 39   Division

$$0.5\overline{)11.5} \longrightarrow 0.5\overline{)11.5} \longrightarrow 5\overline{)115}$$

Multiply
by 10.

$$\begin{array}{r} 23 \\ 5\overline{)115} \\ \underline{100} \\ 15 \\ \underline{15} \\ 0 \end{array}$$

$$0.06\overline{)0.426} \longrightarrow 0.06\overline{)0.426} \longrightarrow 6\overline{)42.6}$$

Multiply
by 100.

$$\begin{array}{r} 7.1 \\ 6\overline{)42.6} \\ \underline{420} \\ 6 \\ \underline{6} \\ 0 \end{array}$$

$$0.003\overline{)2.1} \longrightarrow 0.003\overline{)2.100} \longrightarrow 3\overline{)2100}$$

Multiply
by 1,000.

$$\begin{array}{r} 700 \\ 3\overline{)2100} \\ \underline{2100} \\ 0 \end{array}$$

Divide.

	a	b	c	d
1.	$0.4\overline{)7.2}$	$0.3\overline{)0.8\,1}$	$0.8\overline{)0.3\,9\,2}$	$0.6\overline{)5\,5.2}$
2.	$0.06\overline{)0.8\,4}$	$0.04\overline{)0.0\,6\,8}$	$0.08\overline{)0.2\,2\,4}$	$0.07\overline{)2.5\,2}$
3.	$0.002\overline{)0.0\,0\,8}$	$0.007\overline{)0.0\,0\,4\,2}$	$0.008\overline{)0.1\,4\,4}$	$0.009\overline{)0.0\,3\,3\,3}$
4.	$0.004\overline{)0.0\,9\,6}$	$0.09\overline{)6.3}$	$0.006\overline{)0.0\,0\,9}$	$0.7\overline{)8.4}$

50

Lesson 40   Division

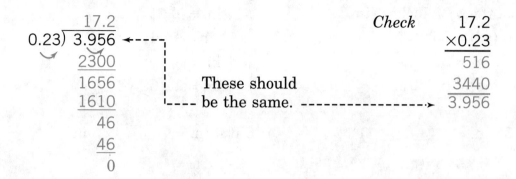

Divide. Check each answer.

        a   *b*   *c*

1. $0.73\overline{)\,5.9\,8\,6}$ $5.6\overline{)\,0.6\,7\,2}$ $0.15\overline{)\,7\,5}$

2. $2.1\overline{)\,6.9\,3}$ $0.15\overline{)\,1\,8}$ $0.083\overline{)\,6.3\,0\,8}$

3. $0.37\overline{)\,0.1\,7\,3\,9}$ $1.6\overline{)\,4.4\,8}$ $0.53\overline{)\,4.8\,7\,6}$

NAME _____

Lesson 41   Length

1 foot (ft) = 12 inches (in.)
1 yard (yd) = 3 ft
1 yd = 36 in.
1 mile (mi) = 5,280 ft

1 in. = $\frac{1}{12}$ ft
1 ft = $\frac{1}{3}$ yd
1 in. = $\frac{1}{36}$ yd
1 mi = 1,760 yd

36 in. = ____?____ ft

1 in. = $\frac{1}{12}$ ft

(36×1) in. = $(36 \times \frac{1}{12})$ ft

36 in. = ____3____ ft

6 ft 4 in. = ____?____ in.

1 ft = 12 in.

6 ft = (6×12) or 72 in.

6 ft 4 in. = $(72 + 4)$ in.

6 ft 4 in. = ____76____ in.

Complete the following.

a

1. 6 ft = _____ in.

2. 9 yd = _____ ft

3. 5 yd = _____ in.

4. 3 mi = _____ ft

5. 5 yd = _____ ft

6. 2 mi = _____ ft

7. 5 ft 4 in. = _____ in.

8. 3 yd 5 in. = _____ in.

9. 5 yd 2 ft = _____ ft

10. 9 ft 6 in. = _____ in.

11. 1 mi 750 ft = _____ ft

b

60 in. = _____ ft

12 ft = _____ yd

144 in. = _____ yd

3 mi = _____ yd

18 in. = _____ ft

5 mi = _____ yd

Lesson 42 Area PRE-ALGEBRA

To determine the *area measure* (*A*) of a right triangle, find *one-half* the product of the measure of its *base* (*b*) and the measure of its *height* (*h*).

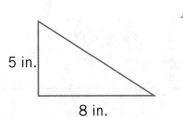

$A = \frac{1}{2} \times b \times h$
$= \frac{1}{2} \times (8 \times 5)$
$= \frac{1}{2} \times 40$
$= 20$

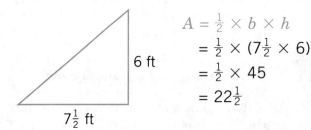

$A = \frac{1}{2} \times b \times h$
$= \frac{1}{2} \times (7\frac{1}{2} \times 6)$
$= \frac{1}{2} \times 45$
$= 22\frac{1}{2}$

The area is ____20____ square inches.

The area is ___$22\frac{1}{2}$___ square feet.

Find the area of each right triangle below.

1.

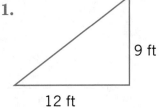

a

9 ft

12 ft

_____ square feet

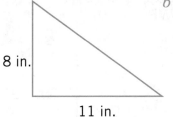

b

8 in.

11 in.

_____ square inches

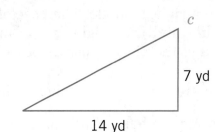

c

7 yd

14 yd

_____ square yards

2.

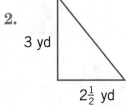

3 yd

$2\frac{1}{2}$ yd

_____ square yards

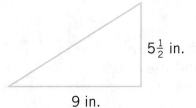

$5\frac{1}{2}$ in.

9 in.

_____ square inches

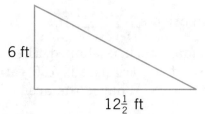

6 ft

$12\frac{1}{2}$ ft

_____ square feet

Find the area of each right triangle described below.

	base	height	area
3.	8 ft	9 ft	_____ square feet
4.	7 yd	5 yd	_____ square yards
5.	$4\frac{1}{2}$ in.	6 in.	_____ square inches
6.	5 ft	$3\frac{1}{2}$ ft	_____ square feet
7.	$3\frac{3}{4}$ in.	2 in.	_____ square inches

Problem Solving   PRE-ALGEBRA

Solve each problem. Use the space at the right to work each problem.

1. The edges of a flower garden form a right triangle. The base of the triangle is 16 feet and the height is 8 feet. What is the area of the garden?

   The area is _____ square feet.

   1.

2. A sailboat has a sail that is shaped like a right triangle. The base of the triangle is 14 feet and the height is 20 feet. What is the area of the sail?

   The area is _____ square feet.

   2.

3. Anne has a piece of poster board that is shaped like a right triangle. The base of the triangle is 28 inches and the height is $16\frac{1}{2}$ inches. What is the area of the piece of poster board?

   The area is _____ square inches.

   3.

4. Mr. McKee has a patio that is shaped like a right triangle. The base of the triangle is 36 feet and the height is 12 feet. What is the area of the patio?

   The area is _____ square feet.

   4.

5. A small park is shaped like a right triangle. The base of the triangle is 160 yards and the height is 120 yards. What is the area of the park?

   The area is _____ square yards.

   5.

6. Nelson has a piece of sheet metal that is shaped like a right triangle. The base of the triangle is 16 inches and the height is $12\frac{1}{2}$ inches. What is the area of the piece of sheet metal?

   The area is _____ square inches.

   6.

7. Mrs. Jones has a piece of material that is shaped like a right triangle. The base of the triangle is $25\frac{1}{2}$ inches and the height is 18 inches. What is the area of the piece of material?

   The area is _____ square inches.

   7.

Lesson 43 Area and Volume   PRE-ALGEBRA

Find the area of each right triangle or rectangle below.

| | *a* | *b* | *c* |

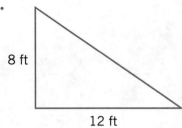

8 ft

12 ft

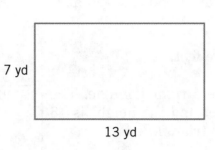

7 yd

13 yd

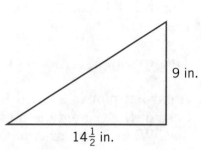

9 in.

$14\frac{1}{2}$ in.

_____ square feet   _____ square yards   _____ square inches

2.

11 yd

$7\frac{1}{2}$ yd

6 in.

$9\frac{1}{2}$ in.

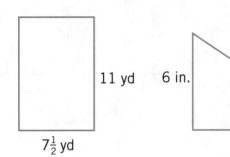

$7\frac{1}{2}$ ft

$7\frac{1}{2}$ ft

_____ square yards   _____ square inches   _____ square feet

Find the volume of each rectangular solid described below.

	length	width	height	volume
3.	7 yd	5 yd	3 yd	_____ cubic yards
4.	9 in.	5 in.	$4\frac{1}{2}$ in.	_____ cubic inches
5.	6 ft	$3\frac{1}{4}$ ft	9 ft	_____ cubic feet
6.	$5\frac{1}{2}$ yd	3 yd	7 yd	_____ cubic yards
7.	$3\frac{1}{4}$ in.	$2\frac{3}{4}$ in.	4 in.	_____ cubic inches
8.	$6\frac{1}{2}$ ft	5 ft	$4\frac{1}{2}$ ft	_____ cubic feet
9.	3 in.	$5\frac{1}{4}$ in.	$3\frac{1}{2}$ in.	_____ cubic inches
10.	$9\frac{1}{4}$ ft	$8\frac{3}{4}$ ft	5 ft	_____ cubic feet

Problem Solving   PRE-ALGEBRA

Solve each problem. Use the space at the right to work each problem.

1. A basketball court is shaped like a rectangle. The length is 84 feet and the width is 50 feet. What is the area of the court?

   The area is _____ square feet.

   1.

2. A garden plot is shaped like a right triangle. The base of the triangle is 50 feet and the height is 18 feet. What is the area of the triangle?

   The area is _____ square feet.

   2.

3. A suitcase is 32 inches long, 16 inches wide, and 6 inches deep. What is the volume of the suitcase?

   The volume is _____ cubic inches.

   3.

4. Mrs. Langley has a flower bed that is shaped like a right triangle. The base of the triangle is $12\frac{1}{2}$ feet and the height is 6 feet. What is the area of the flower bed?

   The area is _____ square feet.

   4.

5. A plot of land is shaped like a rectangle. It is 280 yards long and 90 yards wide. What is the area of the plot?

   The area is _____ square yards.

   5.

6. A box is 9 inches long, $6\frac{1}{2}$ inches wide, and $1\frac{1}{2}$ inches deep. What is the volume of the box?

   The volume is _____ cubic inches.

   6.

7. A rectangular tabletop is 72 inches long and 36 inches wide. What is the area of the tabletop?

   The area is _____ square inches.

   7.

8. A brick is 8 inches long, 3 inches wide, and 2 inches high. How much space does the brick occupy?

   The brick occupies _____ cubic inches of space.

   8.

Lesson 44 Capacity

| 1 pint (pt) = 2 cups |
| 1 quart (qt) = 2 pt |
| 1 gallon (gal) = 4 qt |

| 1 cup = $\frac{1}{2}$ pt |
| 1 pt = $\frac{1}{2}$ qt |
| 1 qt = $\frac{1}{4}$ gal |

5 pt = _____?_____ qt

1 pt = $\frac{1}{2}$ qt
5 pt = ($\frac{1}{2}$ × 5) qt

5 pt = ___$2\frac{1}{2}$___ qt

3 gal 2 qt = _____?_____ qt

1 gal = 4 qt
3 gal = (3 × 4) or 12 qt
3 gal 2 qt = (12 + 2) qt

3 gal 2 qt = ___14___ qt

Complete the following.

a | b

1. 3 pt = _____ cups   8 cups = _____ pt

2. 5 qt = _____ pt   10 pt = _____ qt

3. 4 gal = _____ qt   11 qt = _____ gal

4. 24 qt = _____ gal   15 pt = _____ qt

5. 2 pt 1 cup = _____ cups

6. 5 gal 3 qt = _____ qt

7. 2 qt 1 pt = _____ pt

8. 4 gal 3 qt = _____ qt

9. An aquarium holds 3 gallons 3 quarts of water.
   How many quarts would this be? How many pints?
   How many cups?

   This would be _____ quarts.

   This would be _____ pints.

   This would be _____ cups.

Lesson 45   Weight and Time

| 1 pound (lb) = 16 ounces (oz) |
| 1 ton = 2,000 lb |

$$1 \text{ oz} = \tfrac{1}{16} \text{ lb}$$

| 1 minute (min) = 60 seconds (sec) |
| 1 hour = 60 min |
| 1 day = 24 hours |

$$1 \text{ sec} = \tfrac{1}{60} \text{ min}$$
$$1 \text{ min} = \tfrac{1}{60} \text{ hour}$$
$$1 \text{ hour} = \tfrac{1}{24} \text{ day}$$

80 oz = ___?___ lb

$1 \text{ oz} = \tfrac{1}{16} \text{ lb}$
$80 \text{ oz} = (80 \times \tfrac{1}{16}) \text{ lb}$

80 oz = ___5___ lb

1 min 12 sec = ___?___ sec

$1 \text{ min} = 60 \text{ sec}$
$1 \text{ min } 12 \text{ sec} = (60 + 12) \text{ sec}$

1 min 12 sec = ___72___ sec

Complete the following.

	a		b
1.	72 lb = _____ oz		80 oz = _____ lb
2.	4 tons = _____ lb		6,000 lb = _____ tons
3.	3 min = _____ sec		120 sec = _____ min
4.	5 hours = _____ min		360 min = _____ hours
5.	5 days = _____ hours		144 hours = _____ days
6.	3 lb 12 oz = _____ oz		5 lb 6 oz = _____ oz
7.	3 tons 500 lb = _____ lb		
8.	2 hr 45 min = _____ min		
9.	4 days 12 hours = _____ hours		
10.	4 hours 20 min = _____ min		
11.	2 days 8 hours = _____ hours		

Lesson 46 Percent

The symbol % (read **percent**) means $\frac{1}{100}$ or 0.01.

$3\% = 3 \times \frac{1}{100}$ or $3\% = 3 \times 0.01$

$= \underline{\frac{3}{100}}$ $= \underline{\quad 0.03 \quad}$

$17\% = 17 \times \frac{1}{100}$ or $17\% = 17 \times 0.01$

$= \underline{\frac{17}{100}}$ $= \underline{\quad 0.17 \quad}$

Complete the following.

	percent	fraction	decimal
1.	1%		
2.	7%		
3.	29%		
4.	47%		
5.	53%		
6.	21%		
7.	83%		
8.	49%		
9.	61%		
10.	9%		
11.	37%		
12.	77%		
13.	91%		
14.	33%		

59

Lesson 47 Percent and Fractions

Study how a percent is changed to a fraction or mixed numeral in simplest form.

$$75\% = 75 \times \tfrac{1}{100}$$
$$= \tfrac{75}{100}$$
$$= \underline{\quad \tfrac{3}{4} \quad}$$

$$125\% = 125 \times \tfrac{1}{100}$$
$$= \tfrac{125}{100}$$
$$= \tfrac{5}{4} \text{ or } \underline{\quad 1\tfrac{1}{4} \quad}$$

Study how a fraction or mixed numeral is changed to a percent.

$$\tfrac{1}{2} = \tfrac{1}{2} \times \tfrac{50}{50}$$
$$= \tfrac{50}{100}$$
$$= 50 \times \tfrac{1}{100}$$
$$= \underline{\quad 50 \quad}\%$$

$$1\tfrac{3}{4} = \tfrac{7}{4} \times \tfrac{25}{25}$$
$$= \tfrac{175}{100}$$
$$= 175 \times \tfrac{1}{100}$$
$$= \underline{\quad 1.75 \quad}\%$$

Change each of the following to a fraction or mixed numeral in simplest form.

	a	*b*	*c*
1.	25% = _____	45% = _____	160% = _____
2.	65% = _____	120% = _____	24% = _____
3.	78% = _____	55% = _____	260% = _____
4.	70% = _____	144% = _____	86% = _____
5.	95% = _____	40% = _____	180% = _____

Change each of the following to a percent.

	a	*b*	*c*
6.	$\tfrac{1}{5}$ = _____	$\tfrac{3}{4}$ = _____	$\tfrac{1}{20}$ = _____
7.	$2\tfrac{7}{50}$ = _____	$\tfrac{3}{5}$ = _____	$1\tfrac{1}{5}$ = _____
8.	$\tfrac{9}{10}$ = _____	$\tfrac{7}{25}$ = _____	$2\tfrac{1}{4}$ = _____
9.	$1\tfrac{3}{5}$ = _____	$\tfrac{3}{10}$ = _____	$\tfrac{4}{25}$ = _____
10.	$\tfrac{7}{20}$ = _____	$\tfrac{31}{50}$ = _____	$1\tfrac{2}{5}$ = _____

Lesson 48   Percent and Decimals

Study how a percent is changed to a decimal.

$12.5\% = 12.5 \times 0.01$ $1.25\% = 1.25 \times 0.01$

$= \underline{0.125}$ $= \underline{0.0125}$

Study how a decimal is changed to a percent.

$0.7 = 0.70$ $0.245 = 24.5 \times 0.01$
$ = 70 \times 0.01$

$= \underline{70\%}$ $= \underline{24.5}\%$

Change each of the following to a decimal.

	a	*b*	*c*
1.	13.5% = _____	37% = _____	6.25% = _____
2.	6.5% = _____	4.75% = _____	2.75% = _____
3.	7% = _____	62.5% = _____	8.5% = _____
4.	32.5% = _____	8.75% = _____	9.5% = _____
5.	8.25% = _____	17.5% = _____	3.75% = _____
6.	0.75% = _____	7.25% = _____	1.75% = _____

Change each of the following to a percent.

	a	*b*	*c*
7.	0.6 = _____	0.52 = _____	0.325 = _____
8.	0.2475 = _____	0.8 = _____	0.65 = _____
9.	0.145 = _____	0.1675 = _____	0.5 = _____
10.	0.06 = _____	0.007 = _____	0.0625 = _____
11.	0.075 = _____	0.0075 = _____	0.005 = _____
12.	0.9 = _____	0.19 = _____	0.385 = _____

NAME _____

Lesson 49 Lines, Line Segments, and Rays

Line AB (denoted $\overleftrightarrow{AB}$) names the line that passes through points A and B. Notice that $\overleftrightarrow{AB}$ and $\overleftrightarrow{BA}$ name the same line.

Line segment CD (denoted $\overline{CD}$) consists of points C and D and all points on the line between C and D. Notice that $\overline{CD}$ and $\overline{DC}$ name the same line segment.

Ray EF (denoted $\overrightarrow{EF}$) consists of point E and all points of $\overleftrightarrow{EF}$ that are on the same side of E as F. Notice that $\overrightarrow{EF}$ and $\overrightarrow{FE}$ do **not** name the same ray.

Complete the following as shown.

		a	*b*

1. line $\underline{JW}$ or $\underline{WJ}$ $\underline{\overleftrightarrow{JW}}$ or $\underline{\overleftrightarrow{WJ}}$

2. ray_____   ____

3. line segment ____ or ____   ____ or ____

4. line segment ____ or ____   ____ or ____

5. line ____ or ____   ____ or ____

6. ray _____   ____

7. ray _____   ____

8. line segment ____ or ____   ____ or ____

62

Lesson 50   Angles

An **angle** is formed by two rays that have a common endpoint. Angle RTS (denoted ∠RTS) is formed by ray TR and ray TS.

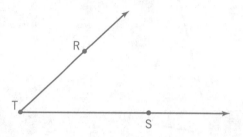

Does ∠STR name the same angle as ∠RTS? _____yes_____

You can find the measure of an angle with a protractor.

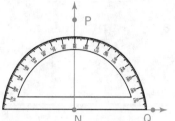

If the measure of an angle is 90°, the angle is a **right angle**.

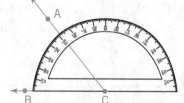

If the measure of an angle is less than 90°, the angle is an **acute angle**.

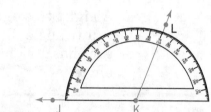

If the measure of an angle is greater than 90°, the angle is an **obtuse angle**.

Name each angle. Find the measure of each angle. Write whether the angle is right, acute, or obtuse.

1.   This symbol shows that this is a right angle.   ∠_____ or ∠_____   _____° _____

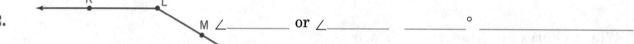

2.   ∠_____ or ∠_____   _____° _____

3.   ∠_____ or ∠_____   _____° _____

4.   ∠_____ or ∠_____   _____° _____

5.   ∠_____ or ∠_____   _____° _____

Lesson 51 Triangles and Quadrilaterals

  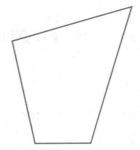  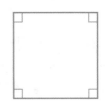

A triangle has 3 sides.

A right triangle is a triangle that has 1 right angle.

A quadrilateral has 4 sides.

A rectangle is a quadrilateral that has 4 right angles.

A square is a rectangle that has 4 sides that are all the same length.

Use the figures below to answer each question. You may use some letters more than once. You may not use all of the letters.

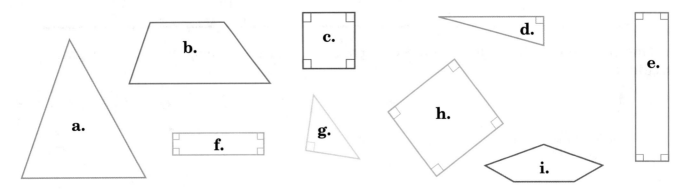

1. Which figures are triangles? _____

2. Which figures are right triangles? _____

3. Which figures are quadrilaterals? _____

4. Which figures are rectangles? _____

5. Which figures are squares? _____

6. Which figures are triangles, but not right triangles? _____

7. Which figures are quadrilaterals, but are not rectangles? _____

ANSWER KEY

Lesson 1 Addition and Subtraction

Add or subtract.

	a	b	c	d	e	f
1.	32 +6 = 38	5 +48 = 53	23 +35 = 58	47 +26 = 73	89 +50 = 139	78 +57 = 135
2.	58 −3 = 55	72 −21 = 51	47 −38 = 9	159 −93 = 66	143 −85 = 58	202 −37 = 165
3.	523 +364 = 887	428 +537 = 965	683 +194 = 877	385 +276 = 661	483 +629 = 1112	753 +869 = 1622
4.	783 −502 = 281	926 −418 = 508	564 −283 = 281	1925 −137 = 1788	2436 −648 = 1788	1926 −928 = 998
5.	5231 +3468 = 8699	4661 +2179 = 6840	3157 +6930 = 10087	2087 +9237 = 11324	4281 +6759 = 11040	
6.	8426 −3312 = 5114	7531 −3452 = 4079	8426 −2756 = 5670	13041 −9158 = 3883	25308 −8499 = 16809	
7.	63125 +10420 = 73545	42163 +45387 = 87550	28135 +47385 = 75520	61702 +28715 = 90417	37839 +57893 = 95732	
8.	72519 −30418 = 42101	83162 −35087 = 48075	52083 −41839 = 10244	98035 −68746 = 29289	63613 −55895 = 7718	
9.	23 34 +42 = 99	426 709 +358 = 1493	4216 5384 +2196 = 11796	22514 43868 +21706 = 88088	82965 372 +1451 = 84788	

3

Problem Solving

Answer each question. Use the space at the right to work each problem.

1. In a contest, Cara earned 758 points. Kelley earned 929 points. Bill earned 1,356 points. How many points did the two girls earn?
Are you to add or subtract? **add**
How many points did the two girls earn? **1687**

2. In problem 1, how many more points did Bill earn than Kelley?
Are you to add or subtract? **subtract**
How many more points did Bill earn than Kelley? **427**

3. In problem 1, how many points did all three people earn?
Are you to add or subtract? **add**
How many points did all three earn? **3043**

4. This month 32,526 people visited the museum. Last month 28,831 people visited the museum. How many more people visited the museum this month than last month?
Are you to add or subtract? **subtract**
How many more people visited the museum this month than last month? **3695**

5. In problem 4, how many people visited the museum during the two months?
Are you to add or subtract? **add**
How many people visited the museum during the two months? **61357**

6. At the beginning of last year 52,116 cars were registered. There were 4,913 new cars registered the first six months and 3,085 the second six months. How many cars were registered at the end of the year?
Are you to add or subtract? **add**
How many cars were registered at the end of the year? **60114**

4

Lesson 2 Multiplication

Multiply.

	a	b	c	d	e	f	g	h
1.	4 ×0 = 0	2 ×0 = 0	8 ×0 = 0	1 ×0 = 0	7 ×1 = 7	6 ×1 = 6	1 ×1 = 1	5 ×1 = 5
2.	8 ×2 = 16	2 ×2 = 4	4 ×2 = 8	7 ×2 = 14	6 ×2 = 12	5 ×2 = 10	3 ×2 = 6	9 ×2 = 18
3.	9 ×3 = 27	7 ×3 = 21	5 ×3 = 15	0 ×3 = 0	1 ×3 = 3	6 ×3 = 18	4 ×3 = 12	3 ×3 = 9
4.	4 ×4 = 16	3 ×4 = 12	5 ×4 = 20	8 ×4 = 32	7 ×4 = 28	0 ×4 = 0	9 ×4 = 36	1 ×4 = 4
5.	8 ×5 = 40	2 ×5 = 10	7 ×5 = 35	5 ×5 = 25	4 ×5 = 20	3 ×5 = 15	1 ×5 = 5	0 ×5 = 0
6.	8 ×6 = 48	2 ×6 = 12	9 ×6 = 54	7 ×6 = 42	6 ×6 = 36	5 ×6 = 30	1 ×6 = 6	3 ×6 = 18
7.	9 ×7 = 63	7 ×7 = 49	6 ×7 = 42	0 ×7 = 0	1 ×7 = 7	5 ×7 = 35	8 ×7 = 56	4 ×7 = 28
8.	0 ×8 = 0	5 ×8 = 40	8 ×8 = 64	9 ×8 = 72	4 ×8 = 32	3 ×8 = 24	6 ×8 = 48	7 ×8 = 56
9.	3 ×9 = 27	9 ×9 = 81	8 ×9 = 72	1 ×9 = 9	2 ×9 = 18	7 ×9 = 63	6 ×9 = 54	4 ×9 = 36

5

Lesson 3 Division

Divide.

	a	b	c	d	e	f	g	h
1.	1)2 = 2	1)3 = 3	1)5 = 5	1)4 = 4	1)6 = 6	1)9 = 9	1)8 = 8	1)1 = 1
2.	2)18 = 9	2)12 = 6	2)14 = 7	2)16 = 8	2)8 = 4	2)10 = 5	2)4 = 2	2)2 = 1
3.	3)0 = 0	3)15 = 5	3)9 = 3	3)12 = 4	3)24 = 8	3)18 = 6	3)3 = 1	3)21 = 7
4.	4)20 = 5	4)8 = 2	4)4 = 1	4)12 = 3	4)32 = 8	4)24 = 6	4)36 = 9	4)4 = 1
5.	5)30 = 6	5)45 = 9	5)0 = 0	5)10 = 2	5)25 = 5	5)15 = 3	5)40 = 8	5)5 = 1
6.	6)30 = 5	6)42 = 7	6)6 = 1	6)36 = 6	6)54 = 9	6)48 = 8		
7.	7)0 = 0	7)21 = 3	7)14 = 2	7)56 = 8	7)49 = 7	7)63 = 9	7)35 = 5	7)28 = 4
8.	8)16 = 2	8)0 = 0	8)56 = 7	8)72 = 9	8)48 = 6	8)32 = 4	8)24 = 3	8)40 = 5
9.	9)45 = 5	9)27 = 3	9)36 = 4	9)63 = 7	9)9 = 1	9)81 = 9	9)0 = 0	9)54 = 6

6

Lesson 4 Multiplication

Multiply 7 ones by 5.
9817 ×5 = 5

Multiply 1 ten by 5. Add the 3 tens.
9817 ×5 = 85

Multiply 8 hundreds by 5.
9817 ×5 = 085, 800 ×5 = 4000

Multiply 9 thousands by 5. Add the 4 thousands.
9817 ×5 = 49085, +4000 = 49000

Multiply.

	a	b	c	d	e
1.	32 ×3 = 96	23 ×4 = 92	82 ×3 = 246	78 ×8 = 624	95 ×6 = 570
2.	421 ×2 = 842	123 ×4 = 492	241 ×3 = 723	501 ×5 = 2505	159 ×6 = 954
3.	783 ×3 = 2349	538 ×8 = 4304	762 ×5 = 3810	954 ×7 = 6678	473 ×9 = 4257
4.	1033 ×2 = 2066	3216 ×3 = 9648	3172 ×3 = 9516	5014 ×2 = 10028	3257 ×3 = 9771
5.	1478 ×6 = 8868	5738 ×7 = 40166	4826 ×9 = 43434	5384 ×6 = 32304	7083 ×5 = 35415

7

Lesson 5 Multiplication

Multiply 4567 by 1.
4567 ×321: 4567, 4567, 4567 = 91340

Multiply 4567 by 20.
4567 ×321: 4567, 91340, 1370100

Multiply 4567 by 300.
4567 ×321: 91340, 1370100; Add. 1,466,007

Multiply.

	a	b	c	d	e
1.	57 ×21 = 1197	48 ×32 = 1536	75 ×63 = 4725	135 ×48 = 6480	276 ×42 = 11592
2.	531 ×27 = 14337	835 ×92 = 76820	1864 ×27 = 50328	3186 ×54 = 172044	7083 ×92 = 651636
3.	413 ×214 = 88382	564 ×532 = 300048	217 ×416 = 90272	908 ×592 = 537536	
4.	1564 ×795 = 1243380	3827 ×630 = 2411010	9216 ×205 = 1889280	5043 ×684 = 3449412	

8

65

ANSWER KEY

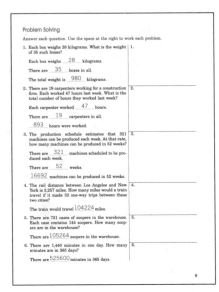

Problem Solving

Answer each question. Use the space at the right to work each problem.

1. Each box weighs 28 kilograms. What is the weight of 35 such boxes?

   Each box weighs __28__ kilograms.

   There are __35__ boxes in all.

   The total weight is __980__ kilograms.

2. There are 19 carpenters working for a construction firm. Each worked 47 hours last week. What is the total number of hours they worked last week?

   Each carpenter worked __47__ hours.

   There are __19__ carpenters in all.

   __893__ hours were worked.

3. The production schedule estimates that 321 machines can be produced each week. At that rate, how many machines can be produced in 52 weeks?

   There are __321__ machines scheduled to be produced each week.

   There are __52__ weeks.

   __16692__ machines can be produced in 52 weeks.

4. The rail distance between Los Angeles and New York is 3,257 miles. How many miles would a train travel if it made 32 one-way trips between these two cities?

   The train would travel __104224__ miles.

5. There are 731 cases of zoopers in the warehouse. Each case contains 144 zoopers. How many zoopers are in the warehouse?

   There are __105264__ zoopers in the warehouse.

6. There are 1,440 minutes in one day. How many minutes are in 365 days?

   There are __525600__ minutes in 365 days.

9

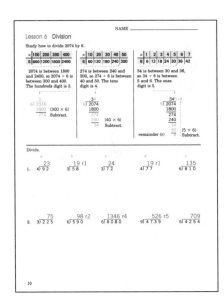

NAME _____

Lesson 6 Division

Study how to divide 2074 by 6.

×	100	200	300	400
6	600	1200	1800	2400

2074 is between 1800 and 2400, so 2074 ÷ 6 is between 300 and 400. The hundreds digit is 3.

×	10	20	30	40	50
6	60	120	180	240	300

274 is between 240 and 300, so 274 ÷ 6 is between 40 and 50. The tens digit is 4.

×	1	2	3	4	5	6	7
6	6	12	18	24	30	36	42

34 is between 30 and 36, so 34 ÷ 6 is between 5 and 6. The ones digit is 5.

Divide.

1.
a. 4)92 = 23
b. 3)58 = 19 r1
c. 3)72 = 24
d. 4)77 = 19 r1
e. 6)810 = 135

2.
a. 3)225 = 75
b. 6)590 = 98 r2
c. 6)8080 = 1346 r4
d. 9)4739 = 526 r5
e. 6)4254 = 709

10

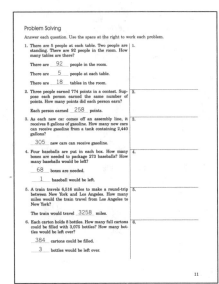

Problem Solving

Answer each question. Use the space at the right to work each problem.

1. There are 5 people at each table. Two people are standing. There are 92 people in the room. How many tables are there?

   There are __92__ people in the room.

   There are __5__ people at each table.

   There are __18__ tables in the room.

2. Three people earned 774 points in a contest. Suppose each person earned the same number of points. How many points did each person earn?

   Each person earned __258__ points.

3. As each new car comes off an assembly line, it receives 8 gallons of gasoline. How many new cars can receive gasoline from a tank containing 2,440 gallons?

   __305__ new cars can receive gasoline.

4. Four baseballs are put in each box. How many boxes are needed to package 273 baseballs? How many baseballs would be left?

   __68__ boxes are needed.

   __1__ baseball would be left.

5. A train travels 6,516 miles to make a round-trip between New York and Los Angeles. How many miles would the train travel from Los Angeles to New York?

   The train would travel __3258__ miles.

6. Each carton holds 8 bottles. How many full cartons could be filled with 3,075 bottles? How many bottles would be left over?

   __384__ cartons could be filled.

   __3__ bottles would be left over.

11

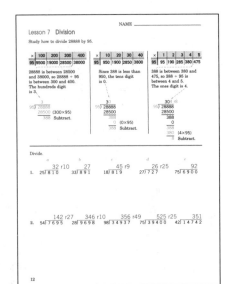

NAME _____

Lesson 7 Division

Study how to divide 28888 by 95.

×	100	200	300	400
95	9500	19000	28500	38000

28888 is between 28500 and 38000, so 28888 ÷ 95 is between 300 and 400. The hundreds digit is 3.

×	10	20	30	40
95	950	1900	2850	3800

Since 388 is less than 950, the tens digit is 0.

×	1	2	3	4	5
95	95	190	285	380	475

388 is between 380 and 475, so 388 ÷ 95 is between 4 and 5. The ones digit is 4.

Divide.

1.
a. 25)810 = 32 r10
b. 33)891 = 27
c. 18)819 = 45 r9
d. 27)727 = 26 r25
e. 75)6900 = 92

2.
a. 54)7695 = 142 r27
b. 28)9698 = 346 r10
c. 98)34937 = 356 r49
d. 75)39400 = 525 r25
e. 42)14742 = 351

12

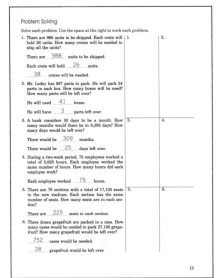

Problem Solving

Solve each problem. Use the space at the right to work each problem.

1. There are 988 units to be shipped. Each crate will hold 26 units. How many crates would be needed to ship all the units?

   There are __988__ units to be shipped.

   Each crate will hold __26__ units.

   __38__ crates will be needed.

2. Mr. Lodey has 987 parts to pack. He will pack 24 parts in each box. How many boxes will he need? How many parts will be left over?

   He will need __41__ boxes.

   He will have __3__ parts left over.

3. A bank considers 30 days to be a month. How many months would there be in 9,295 days? How many days would be left over?

   There would be __309__ months.

   There would be __25__ days left over.

4. During a two-week period, 75 employees worked a total of 5,625 hours. Each employee worked the same number of hours. How many hours did each employee work?

   Each employee worked __75__ hours.

5. There are 76 sections with a total of 17,100 seats in the new stadium. Each section has the same number of seats. How many seats are in each section?

   There are __225__ seats in each section.

6. Three dozen grapefruit are packed in a case. How many cases would be needed to pack 27,100 grapefruit? How many grapefruit would be left over?

   __752__ cases would be needed.

   __28__ grapefruit would be left over.

13

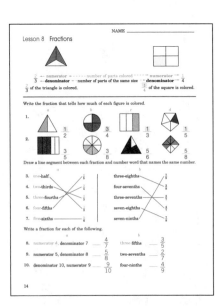

NAME _____

Lesson 8 Fractions

$\frac{2}{3}$ numerator — number of parts colored
      denominator — number of parts of the same size
$\frac{2}{3}$ of the triangle is colored.

$\frac{3}{4}$ numerator
      denominator
$\frac{3}{4}$ of the square is colored.

Write the fraction that tells how much of each figure is colored.

1.
a. $\frac{1}{3}$
b. $\frac{3}{4}$
c. $\frac{1}{4}$
d. $\frac{1}{5}$

2.
a. $\frac{3}{5}$
b. $\frac{3}{8}$
c. $\frac{5}{6}$
d. $\frac{5}{8}$

Draw a line segment between each fraction and number word that names the same number.

3. one-half — three-eighths
4. two-thirds — four-sevenths
5. three-fourths — three-sevenths
6. four-fifths — seven-eighths
7. five-sixths — seven-ninths

Write a fraction for each of the following.

8. numerator 4, denominator 7 $\frac{4}{7}$ three-fifths $\frac{3}{5}$

9. numerator 5, denominator 8 $\frac{5}{8}$ two-sevenths $\frac{2}{7}$

10. denominator 10, numerator 9 $\frac{9}{10}$ four-ninths $\frac{4}{9}$

14

66

ANSWER KEY

Lesson 9 Mixed Numerals

NAME _____

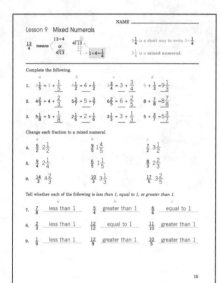

$\frac{13}{4}$ means $4\overline{)13}$ or $\frac{13}{4} = 1 + \frac{4}{4} = 1\frac{1}{4}$

$3\frac{1}{4}$ is a short way to write $3 + \frac{1}{4}$.
$3\frac{1}{4}$ is a mixed numeral.

Complete the following.

	a	b	c	d
1.	$3\frac{1}{5} = 3 + \frac{1}{5}$	$4\frac{1}{2} = 4 + \frac{1}{2}$	$3\frac{3}{4} = 3 + \frac{3}{4}$	$9 + \frac{1}{3} = 9\frac{1}{3}$
2.	$4\frac{2}{3} = 4 + \frac{2}{3}$	$5\frac{3}{7} = 5 + \frac{3}{7}$	$6\frac{2}{5} = 6 + \frac{2}{5}$	$8 + \frac{7}{8} = 8\frac{7}{8}$
3.	$5\frac{1}{8} = 5 + \frac{1}{8}$	$2\frac{1}{6} = 2 + \frac{1}{6}$	$3\frac{1}{3} = 3 + \frac{1}{3}$	$5 + \frac{3}{7} = 5\frac{3}{7}$

Change each fraction to a mixed numeral.

	a	b	c
4.	$\frac{5}{2}$ $2\frac{1}{2}$	$\frac{9}{5}$ $1\frac{4}{5}$	$\frac{7}{2}$ $3\frac{1}{2}$
5.	$\frac{9}{4}$ $2\frac{1}{4}$	$\frac{6}{5}$ $1\frac{1}{5}$	$\frac{8}{3}$ $2\frac{2}{3}$
6.	$\frac{14}{3}$ $4\frac{2}{3}$	$\frac{10}{3}$ $3\frac{1}{3}$	$\frac{17}{5}$ $3\frac{2}{5}$

Tell whether each of the following is *less than 1*, *equal to 1*, or *greater than 1*.

	a	b	c
7.	$\frac{7}{8}$ less than 1	$\frac{5}{4}$ greater than 1	$\frac{6}{6}$ equal to 1
8.	$\frac{2}{3}$ less than 1	$\frac{12}{12}$ equal to 1	$\frac{11}{5}$ greater than 1
9.	$\frac{1}{9}$ less than 1	$\frac{12}{5}$ greater than 1	$\frac{10}{5}$ greater than 1

15

Lesson 10 Addition

NAME _____

$\frac{2}{5} + \frac{1}{5} = \frac{2+1}{5} = \frac{3}{5}$ Add the numerators. Use the same denominator.

$\frac{3}{10} + \frac{4}{10} + \frac{2}{10} = \frac{3+4+2}{10} = \frac{9}{10}$ Use the same denominator.

Add.

	a	b	c	d
1.	$\frac{3}{5} + \frac{1}{5} = \frac{4}{5}$	$\frac{4}{8} + \frac{3}{8} = \frac{7}{8}$	$\frac{2}{7} + \frac{2}{7} = \frac{4}{7}$	$\frac{1}{5} + \frac{1}{5} + \frac{2}{5} = \frac{4}{5}$
2.	$\frac{3}{6} + \frac{2}{6} = \frac{5}{6}$	$\frac{1}{7} + \frac{3}{7} = \frac{4}{7}$	$\frac{2}{8} + \frac{1}{8} = \frac{3}{8}$	$\frac{1}{4} + \frac{1}{4} + \frac{1}{4} = \frac{3}{4}$
3.	$\frac{3}{10} + \frac{4}{10} = \frac{7}{10}$	$\frac{4}{12} + \frac{1}{12} = \frac{5}{12}$	$\frac{5}{11} + \frac{4}{11} = \frac{9}{11}$	$\frac{2}{15} + \frac{5}{15} + \frac{4}{15} = \frac{11}{15}$

	a	b	c	d	e	f
4.	$\frac{4}{6} + \frac{1}{6} = \frac{5}{6}$	$\frac{3}{8} + \frac{4}{8} = \frac{7}{8}$	$\frac{1}{7} + \frac{2}{7} = \frac{3}{7}$	$\frac{3}{10} + \frac{6}{10} = \frac{9}{10}$	$\frac{7}{12} + \frac{4}{12} = \frac{11}{12}$	$\frac{3}{11} + \frac{1}{11} = \frac{4}{11}$
5.	$\frac{1}{5} + \frac{1}{5} + \frac{1}{5} = \frac{3}{5}$	$\frac{2}{7} + \frac{3}{7} + \frac{1}{7} = \frac{6}{7}$	$\frac{2}{8} + \frac{1}{8} + \frac{2}{8} = \frac{5}{8}$	$\frac{4}{10} + \frac{1}{10} + \frac{4}{10} = \frac{9}{10}$	$\frac{4}{15} + \frac{4}{15} + \frac{3}{15} = \frac{11}{15}$	$\frac{4}{12} + \frac{2}{12} + \frac{1}{12} = \frac{7}{12}$

16

Lesson 11 Mixed Numerals to Fractions

NAME _____

$3\frac{1}{6} = \frac{(6 \times 3) + 1}{6}$ Multiply the denominator by the whole number and add the numerator.

$= \frac{18 + 1}{6}$
$= \frac{19}{6}$ Use the same denominator.

Change each mixed numeral to a fraction.

	a	b	c
1.	$2\frac{5}{8} = \frac{21}{8}$	$2\frac{3}{5} = \frac{13}{5}$	$3\frac{2}{3} = \frac{11}{3}$
2.	$3\frac{7}{10} = \frac{37}{10}$	$10\frac{2}{3} = \frac{32}{3}$	$14\frac{1}{2} = \frac{29}{2}$
3.	$6\frac{7}{8} = \frac{55}{8}$	$5\frac{9}{10} = \frac{59}{10}$	$13\frac{5}{12} = \frac{161}{12}$
4.	$4\frac{5}{6} = \frac{29}{6}$	$7\frac{3}{4} = \frac{31}{4}$	$8\frac{11}{12} = \frac{107}{12}$

17

Lesson 12 Multiplication

NAME _____

Multiply the numerators.
$\frac{2}{3} \times \frac{4}{5} = \frac{2 \times 4}{3 \times 5} = \frac{8}{15}$
Multiply the denominators.

$\frac{1}{2} \times \frac{3}{4} = \frac{3}{2 \times 4} = \frac{3}{8}$
$\frac{2}{5} \times \frac{1}{3} = \frac{2 \times 1}{5 \times 3} = \frac{2}{15}$

Multiply.

	a	b	c	d
1.	$\frac{1}{2} \times \frac{1}{3} = \frac{1}{6}$	$\frac{3}{4} \times \frac{1}{2} = \frac{3}{8}$	$\frac{1}{3} \times \frac{1}{4} = \frac{1}{12}$	$\frac{3}{5} \times \frac{1}{2} = \frac{3}{10}$
2.	$\frac{3}{5} \times \frac{3}{4} = \frac{9}{20}$	$\frac{4}{7} \times \frac{3}{5} = \frac{12}{35}$	$\frac{4}{5} \times \frac{2}{3} = \frac{8}{15}$	$\frac{3}{8} \times \frac{5}{7} = \frac{15}{56}$
3.	$\frac{2}{3} \times \frac{4}{5} = \frac{8}{15}$	$\frac{1}{8} \times \frac{1}{2} = \frac{1}{16}$	$\frac{5}{7} \times \frac{3}{4} = \frac{15}{28}$	$\frac{3}{5} \times \frac{7}{8} = \frac{21}{40}$
4.	$\frac{6}{7} \times \frac{3}{5} = \frac{18}{35}$	$\frac{2}{9} \times \frac{1}{3} = \frac{2}{27}$	$\frac{5}{8} \times \frac{3}{7} = \frac{15}{56}$	$\frac{2}{5} \times \frac{3}{7} = \frac{6}{35}$
5.	$\frac{7}{8} \times \frac{7}{8} = \frac{49}{64}$	$\frac{2}{3} \times \frac{2}{3} = \frac{4}{9}$	$\frac{4}{9} \times \frac{2}{3} = \frac{8}{27}$	$\frac{4}{7} \times \frac{6}{5} = \frac{24}{35}$
6.	$\frac{8}{9} \times \frac{5}{7} = \frac{40}{63}$	$\frac{5}{8} \times \frac{1}{3} = \frac{5}{24}$	$\frac{5}{6} \times \frac{5}{7} = \frac{25}{42}$	$\frac{3}{8} \times \frac{5}{8} = \frac{15}{64}$

18

Lesson 13 Simplest Form

NAME _____

A fraction is in simplest form when its numerator and denominator have no common factors, except 1.

A mixed numeral is in simplest form when its fraction is in simplest form and names a number less than 1.

Divide 12 and 15 by their greatest common factor.
$\frac{12}{15} = \frac{12 \div 3}{15 \div 3} = \frac{4}{5}$
The simplest form for $\frac{12}{15}$ is $\frac{4}{5}$.

Divide 4 and 6 by their greatest common factor.
$3\frac{4}{6} = 3 + \frac{4}{6}$
$= 3 + \frac{2}{3}$
$= 3\frac{2}{3}$
The simplest form for $3\frac{4}{6}$ is $3\frac{2}{3}$.

Change each of the following to simplest form.

	a	b	c
1.	$\frac{8}{10}$ $\frac{4}{5}$	$\frac{10}{20}$ $\frac{1}{2}$	$\frac{14}{21}$ $\frac{2}{3}$
2.	$2\frac{4}{8}$ $2\frac{1}{2}$	$3\frac{6}{9}$ $3\frac{2}{3}$	$5\frac{8}{10}$ $5\frac{4}{5}$
3.	$\frac{12}{18}$ $\frac{2}{3}$	$5\frac{9}{12}$ $5\frac{3}{4}$	$\frac{15}{18}$ $\frac{5}{6}$
4.	$6\frac{8}{12}$ $6\frac{2}{3}$	$\frac{25}{30}$ $\frac{5}{6}$	$3\frac{12}{16}$ $3\frac{3}{4}$
5.	$\frac{24}{30}$ $\frac{4}{5}$	$3\frac{14}{18}$ $3\frac{7}{9}$	$\frac{16}{32}$ $\frac{1}{2}$

19

Lesson 14 Multiplication

NAME _____

$\frac{1}{2} \times \frac{3}{4} = \frac{1 \times 3}{2 \times 4} = \frac{3}{8}$
Is $\frac{3}{8}$ in simplest form? yes

$\frac{4}{6} \times \frac{8}{9} = \frac{8}{9}$ ...
Is $\frac{4}{6}$ in simplest form? no
Is $\frac{2}{3}$ in simplest form? yes

Write each answer in simplest form.

	a	b	c	d
1.	$\frac{1}{2} \times \frac{3}{5} = \frac{3}{10}$	$\frac{2}{3} \times \frac{4}{5} = \frac{8}{15}$	$\frac{2}{3} \times \frac{1}{3} = \frac{2}{9}$	$\frac{5}{6} \times \frac{1}{7} = \frac{5}{42}$
2.	$\frac{3}{4} \times \frac{4}{5} = \frac{3}{5}$	$\frac{5}{9} \times \frac{2}{5} = \frac{2}{9}$	$\frac{6}{7} \times \frac{1}{3} = \frac{2}{7}$	$\frac{3}{5} \times \frac{4}{9} = \frac{4}{15}$
3.	$\frac{5}{6} \times \frac{2}{5} = \frac{1}{3}$	$\frac{4}{5} \times \frac{5}{6} = \frac{2}{3}$	$\frac{3}{8} \times \frac{2}{3} = \frac{1}{4}$	$\frac{2}{10} \times \frac{5}{6} = \frac{1}{6}$
4.	$\frac{6}{5} \times \frac{3}{8} = \frac{9}{20}$	$\frac{9}{10} \times \frac{5}{12} = \frac{3}{8}$	$\frac{8}{9} \times \frac{3}{10} = \frac{4}{15}$	$\frac{5}{6} \times \frac{9}{10} = \frac{3}{4}$
5.	$\frac{4}{7} \times \frac{5}{6} = \frac{10}{21}$	$\frac{3}{8} \times \frac{7}{10} = \frac{21}{80}$	$\frac{9}{10} \times \frac{5}{9} = \frac{1}{2}$	$\frac{6}{7} \times \frac{9}{10} = \frac{27}{35}$

20

Answer Key

Problem Solving

Solve. Write each answer in simplest form. Use the space at the right to work each problem.

1. The Urbans had $\frac{3}{4}$ gallon of milk. One-half of this was used for dinner. How much milk was used for dinner? ($\frac{1}{2}$ of $\frac{3}{4} = \frac{1}{2} \times \frac{3}{4}$)

   $\frac{3}{8}$ gallon was used for dinner.

2. Keara read $\frac{4}{5}$ of a book. Two-thirds of that reading was done at school. How much of the book did she read at school?

   She read $\frac{8}{15}$ of the book at school.

3. Tricia lives $\frac{4}{5}$ mile from work. One morning she ran $\frac{1}{2}$ of the distance to work. How far did Tricia run?

   Tricia ran $\frac{2}{5}$ mile.

4. Three-fourths of a room has been painted. Joseph did $\frac{2}{3}$ of the painting. How much of the room did Joseph paint?

   Joseph painted $\frac{1}{2}$ of the room.

5. A truck was carrying $\frac{3}{4}$ ton of sand. One-third of the sand was put into barrels. How much sand was put into barrels?

   $\frac{1}{4}$ ton of sand was put into barrels.

6. Carrie had a rope that was $\frac{2}{3}$ yard long. She used $\frac{1}{2}$ of it. How much rope did she use?

   $\frac{1}{3}$ yard of rope was used.

7. One-fourth of the people in the room have blue eyes. Two-thirds of the blue-eyed people have blond hair. What part of the people in the room have blond hair and blue eyes?

   $\frac{1}{6}$ have blond hair and blue eyes.

21

Lesson 15 Multiplication

$$4 \times \frac{5}{6} = \frac{4}{1} \times \frac{5}{6} \quad \text{Rename whole numbers and mixed numerals as fractions.}$$
$$= \frac{4 \times 5}{1 \times 6} \quad \text{Multiply the fractions.}$$
$$= \frac{20}{6}$$
$$= 3\frac{1}{3} \quad \text{Change to simplest form.}$$

$$4\frac{2}{3} \times 5 = \frac{14}{3} \times \frac{5}{1}$$
$$= \frac{14 \times 5}{3 \times 1}$$
$$= \frac{70}{3}$$
$$= 23\frac{1}{3}$$

Write each answer in simplest form.

	a	b	c	d
1.	$5 \times \frac{2}{3}$ $3\frac{1}{3}$	$6 \times \frac{4}{5}$ $4\frac{4}{5}$	$\frac{1}{2} \times 9$ $4\frac{1}{2}$	$\frac{3}{4} \times 7$ $5\frac{1}{4}$
2.	$9 \times \frac{5}{6}$ $7\frac{1}{2}$	$\frac{1}{4} \times 6$ $1\frac{1}{2}$	$\frac{3}{8} \times 12$ $4\frac{1}{2}$	$10 \times \frac{4}{5}$ 8
3.	$2\frac{1}{2} \times 3$ $7\frac{1}{2}$	$1\frac{1}{3} \times 5$ $6\frac{2}{3}$	$2 \times 3\frac{2}{5}$ $6\frac{4}{5}$	$4 \times 4\frac{2}{3}$ $18\frac{2}{3}$

22

Lesson 16 Multiplication

$$2\frac{3}{5} \times 1\frac{1}{6} = \frac{13}{5} \times \frac{7}{6} \quad \text{Change the mixed numerals to fractions.}$$
$$= \frac{13 \times 7}{5 \times 6} \quad \text{Multiply the fractions.}$$
$$= \frac{91}{30}$$
$$= 3\frac{1}{30} \quad \text{Change to simplest form.}$$

Write each answer in simplest form.

	a	b	c	d
1.	$4\frac{2}{3} \times 1\frac{2}{5}$ $6\frac{8}{15}$	$3\frac{1}{2} \times 1\frac{1}{6}$ $4\frac{1}{12}$	$1\frac{2}{3} \times 2\frac{1}{2}$ $4\frac{1}{6}$	$2\frac{2}{3} \times 2\frac{2}{3}$ $7\frac{1}{9}$
2.	$2\frac{2}{5} \times 2\frac{1}{4}$ $5\frac{2}{5}$	$1\frac{7}{10} \times 2\frac{1}{2}$ $4\frac{1}{4}$	$5\frac{1}{3} \times 1\frac{1}{5}$ $6\frac{2}{5}$	$2\frac{4}{5} \times 1\frac{1}{7}$ $3\frac{1}{5}$
3.	$3\frac{3}{4} \times 2\frac{1}{3}$ $8\frac{3}{4}$	$3\frac{3}{5} \times 1\frac{7}{8}$ $6\frac{3}{8}$	$4\frac{2}{3} \times 1\frac{1}{8}$ $5\frac{1}{4}$	$3\frac{3}{4} \times 3\frac{1}{3}$ $12\frac{1}{2}$
4.	$5\frac{1}{6} \times 6\frac{3}{8}$ $32\frac{15}{16}$	$2\frac{3}{5} \times 2\frac{1}{2}$ $6\frac{1}{2}$	$1\frac{1}{4} \times 1\frac{1}{4}$ $1\frac{9}{16}$	$3\frac{1}{8} \times 6\frac{2}{3}$ $20\frac{5}{6}$

23

Problem Solving

Solve. Write each answer in simplest form. Use the space at the right to work each problem.

1. A full box of soap weighs $2\frac{2}{3}$ pounds. How many pounds would $1\frac{1}{3}$ boxes of soap weigh?

   They would weigh $3\frac{5}{9}$ pounds.

2. It takes $1\frac{4}{5}$ hours to process 1 ton of ore. How many hours would it take to process $3\frac{1}{3}$ tons of ore?

   It would take 6 hours.

3. Each box of bolts weighs $3\frac{3}{4}$ pounds. How many pounds would $8\frac{1}{2}$ boxes of bolts weigh?

   They would weigh $31\frac{7}{8}$ pounds.

4. The boys can walk $3\frac{1}{3}$ miles in 1 hour. At that rate, how many miles could the boys walk in $1\frac{1}{4}$ hours?

   The boys could walk $4\frac{1}{12}$ miles.

5. Each bag of apples weighs $4\frac{1}{2}$ pounds. How much would $3\frac{1}{2}$ bags of apples weigh?

   They would weigh $15\frac{3}{4}$ pounds.

6. Riding her bicycle, Terry averages $9\frac{1}{2}$ miles per hour. At that speed, how far could she go in $2\frac{2}{3}$ hours?

   She could go $25\frac{1}{3}$ miles.

7. In problem 6, suppose Terry averages $9\frac{3}{4}$ miles per hour. How far could she go in $2\frac{2}{3}$ hours?

   She could go 26 miles.

8. A machine can process $2\frac{1}{3}$ tons in 1 hour. How many tons can the machine process in $2\frac{1}{4}$ hours?

   The machine can process $5\frac{1}{4}$ tons in $2\frac{1}{4}$ hours.

9. If the machine in problem 8 broke down after $1\frac{1}{2}$ hours, how many tons would have been processed?

   $3\frac{3}{4}$ tons would have been processed.

24

Lesson 17 Addition and Subtraction

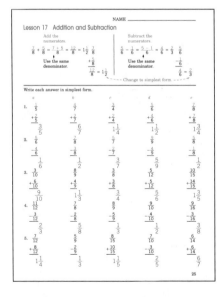

Add the numerators.
$$\frac{7}{8} + \frac{5}{8} = \frac{7+5}{8} = \frac{12}{8} = 1\frac{1}{2}$$
Use the same denominator.

Subtract the numerators.
$$\frac{5}{6} - \frac{1}{6} = \frac{5-1}{6} = \frac{4}{6} = \frac{2}{3}$$
Use the same denominator.
Change to simplest form.

Write each answer in simplest form.

	a	b	c	d	e
1.	$\frac{1}{5} + \frac{4}{5} = \frac{3}{5}$	$\frac{4}{7} + \frac{3}{7} = \frac{6}{7}$	$\frac{3}{4} + \frac{2}{4} = 1\frac{1}{4}$	$\frac{2}{8} + \frac{5}{8} = 1\frac{1}{2}$	$\frac{3}{8} + \frac{5}{8} = 1\frac{3}{4}$
2.	$\frac{2}{3} - \frac{4}{?} = \frac{1}{?}$	$\frac{2}{?} - \frac{3}{?} = \frac{1}{2}$	$\frac{2}{7} - \frac{2}{7} = \frac{3}{7}$	$\frac{4}{9} - \frac{4}{9} = \frac{5}{9}$	$\frac{2}{?} - \frac{1}{?} = \frac{1}{2}$
3.	$\frac{3}{10} + \frac{6}{10} = \frac{9}{10}$	$\frac{8}{9} + \frac{4}{9} = 1\frac{3}{9}$	$\frac{3}{8} + \frac{3}{8} = \frac{3}{4}$	$\frac{5}{12} + \frac{5}{12} = \frac{10}{12}$	$\frac{10}{15} + \frac{14}{15} = \frac{14}{15}$
4.	$\frac{11}{12} - \frac{3}{12} = \frac{2}{3}$	$\frac{7}{8} - \frac{2}{8} = \frac{5}{8}$	$\frac{8}{9} - \frac{5}{9} = \frac{1}{3}$	$\frac{9}{10} - \frac{4}{10} = \frac{1}{2}$	$\frac{9}{16} - \frac{3}{16} = \frac{3}{8}$
5.	$\frac{7}{12} + \frac{8}{12} = 1\frac{1}{4}$	$\frac{7}{15} + \frac{2}{15} = \frac{1}{3}$	$\frac{5}{15} + \frac{10}{15} = \frac{1}{5}$	$\frac{2}{10} + \frac{3}{10} = \frac{2}{5}$	$\frac{6}{14} + \frac{6}{14} = \frac{6}{7}$

25

Lesson 18 Addition and Subtraction

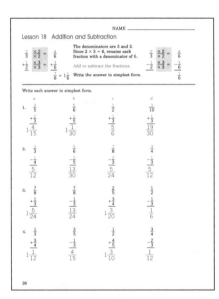

$$\frac{2}{3} = \frac{\times 2}{\times 2} = \frac{4}{6}$$
$$+\frac{1}{2} = \frac{\times 3}{\times 3} = \frac{3}{6}$$
$$\frac{7}{6} = 1\frac{1}{6}$$

The denominators are 3 and 2. Since $2 \times 3 = 6$, rename each fraction with a denominator of 6. Add or subtract the fractions. Write the answer in simplest form.

Write each answer in simplest form.

	a	b	c	d
1.	$\frac{1}{5} + \frac{4}{3} = 1\frac{4}{15}$	$\frac{2}{6} + \frac{1}{3} = 1\frac{1}{30}$	$\frac{1}{2} + \frac{3}{6} = \frac{5}{6}$	$\frac{3}{10} + \frac{3}{5} = \frac{19}{30}$
2.	$\frac{2}{3} - \frac{1}{4} = \frac{5}{12}$	$\frac{2}{6} - \frac{1}{5} = \frac{13}{30}$	$\frac{7}{8} - \frac{2}{6} = \frac{5}{24}$	$\frac{2}{4} - \frac{3}{12} = \frac{5}{12}$
3.	$\frac{7}{8} + \frac{1}{3} = 1\frac{5}{24}$	$\frac{7}{8} + \frac{3}{6} = 1\frac{13}{24}$	$\frac{1}{4} + \frac{3}{5} = 1\frac{1}{20}$	$\frac{1}{2} + \frac{1}{12} = \frac{1}{12}$
4.	$\frac{2}{3} + \frac{3}{4} = 1\frac{1}{12}$	$\frac{3}{5} - \frac{1}{3} = \frac{4}{15}$	$\frac{1}{2} + \frac{4}{5} = 1\frac{3}{10}$	$\frac{3}{4} - \frac{2}{3} = \frac{1}{12}$

26

68

ANSWER KEY

Lesson 19 Addition

NAME _____

$$3\frac{2}{4} \rightarrow 3\frac{4}{8} \qquad 1\frac{1}{2} \rightarrow 1\frac{6}{12}$$
$$+1\frac{1}{8} \rightarrow +1\frac{1}{8} \qquad 3\frac{3}{4} \rightarrow 3\frac{9}{12}$$
$$\overline{4\frac{5}{8}} \qquad\qquad +\frac{2}{3} \rightarrow +\frac{8}{12}$$
$$\overline{4\frac{23}{12}} = 5\frac{11}{12}$$

Rename the numbers so the fractions have the same denominator.
Add the fractions.
Add the whole numbers.

Change to simplest form.

Write each answer in simplest form.

	a	b	c	d
1.	$3\frac{1}{4}$	$3\frac{1}{6}$	$5\frac{1}{2}$	$3\frac{1}{12}$
	$+2\frac{4}{5}$	$+\frac{3}{4}$	$+1\frac{5}{8}$	$+\frac{6}{6}$
	$6\frac{1}{20}$	$3\frac{11}{12}$	$7\frac{1}{8}$	$4\frac{3}{8}$
2.	$9\frac{7}{8}$	$7\frac{2}{5}$	$3\frac{}{}$	$9\frac{9}{10}$
	$+\frac{4}{4}$	$+4\frac{4}{10}$	$+2\frac{6}{8}$	$+3\frac{5}{6}$
	$10\frac{5}{8}$	$11\frac{7}{10}$	$3\frac{13}{30}$	$4\frac{11}{15}$
3.	$6\frac{2}{3}$	$2\frac{1}{5}$	$3\frac{1}{2}$	$\frac{1}{2}$
	$1\frac{3}{4}$	$2\frac{1}{4}$	$5\frac{5}{6}$	$5\frac{1}{5}$
	$+\frac{1}{6}$	$+1\frac{1}{2}$	$+3\frac{7}{12}$	$+1\frac{3}{10}$
	$8\frac{7}{12}$	$5\frac{19}{20}$	$7\frac{3}{4}$	7
4.	$\frac{3}{4}$	$3\frac{5}{8}$	$\frac{1}{4}$	$2\frac{3}{5}$
	$1\frac{2}{3}$	$2\frac{1}{6}$	$1\frac{1}{2}$	$2\frac{1}{2}$
	$+2\frac{1}{5}$	$+\frac{5}{12}$	$+4\frac{7}{8}$	$+3\frac{4}{5}$
	$4\frac{23}{30}$	$6\frac{5}{24}$	$6\frac{5}{8}$	$8\frac{17}{30}$

27

Lesson 20 Subtraction

NAME _____

$$3\frac{2}{3} \rightarrow 3\frac{5}{6} \qquad 3 \rightarrow 2\frac{4}{4}$$
$$-1\frac{1}{6} \rightarrow -1\frac{1}{6} \qquad -\frac{1}{4} \rightarrow -\frac{1}{4}$$
$$\overline{2\frac{3}{6}} = 2\frac{1}{2} \qquad\qquad 2\frac{3}{4}$$

Rename the numbers so the fractions have the same denominator.
Subtract the fractions.
Subtract the whole numbers.

Change to simplest form.

$$3 = 2 + 1$$
$$= 2 + \frac{4}{4}$$
$$= 2\frac{4}{4}$$

Write each answer in simplest form.

	a	b	c	d
1.	7	4	5	8
	$-\frac{3}{4}$	$-\frac{1}{2}$	$-\frac{2}{3}$	$-\frac{1}{8}$
	$6\frac{1}{4}$	$3\frac{1}{2}$	$4\frac{1}{3}$	$7\frac{7}{8}$
2.	$3\frac{4}{5}$	$5\frac{2}{3}$	$4\frac{5}{6}$	$5\frac{9}{10}$
	$-1\frac{1}{2}$	$-3\frac{4}{9}$	$-1\frac{1}{2}$	$-3\frac{2}{5}$
	$2\frac{3}{10}$	$2\frac{2}{9}$	$3\frac{1}{3}$	$2\frac{1}{2}$
3.	5	$6\frac{3}{4}$	$2\frac{2}{3}$	10
	$-\frac{3}{5}$	$-5\frac{1}{8}$	$-1\frac{1}{2}$	$-2\frac{3}{10}$
	$4\frac{2}{5}$	$1\frac{5}{8}$	$1\frac{1}{6}$	$7\frac{7}{10}$
4.	$10\frac{5}{6}$	8	$9\frac{5}{6}$	6
	$-7\frac{5}{12}$	$-\frac{5}{8}$	$-2\frac{1}{3}$	$-\frac{9}{10}$
	$3\frac{5}{12}$	$7\frac{3}{8}$	$7\frac{1}{2}$	$5\frac{1}{10}$

28

Problem Solving

Solve. Write each answer in simplest form. Use the space at the right to work each problem.

1. A CD has been playing for $\frac{1}{2}$ hour. The CD still has $\frac{1}{4}$ hour to play. What is the total length of time the CD can play?

   The CD can play $\underline{\frac{3}{4}}$ hour.

2. It rained $\frac{1}{4}$ inch yesterday and $\frac{1}{5}$ inch today. How much more did it rain yesterday?

   It rained $\underline{\frac{1}{20}}$ inch more yesterday.

3. Matthew spent $\frac{1}{2}$ hour doing his history homework and $\frac{3}{4}$ hour doing his science homework. How much time did he spend doing homework?

   He spent $\underline{1\frac{1}{4}}$ hours doing homework.

4. Rob has a board that is $\frac{1}{2}$ inch too wide. The board is $\frac{1}{8}$ inch wide. What width board does Rob need?

   Rob needs a board $\underline{\frac{5}{8}}$ inch wide.

5. Maranda read $\frac{2}{5}$ hour in the morning and $\frac{1}{2}$ hour in the afternoon. How many hours did she read in the morning and afternoon?

   She read $\underline{\frac{1}{10}}$ hours.

6. In problem 5, how much longer did she read in the morning than in the afternoon?

   She read $\underline{\frac{1}{10}}$ hour longer in the morning.

7. John has two boxes. One weighs $\frac{4}{5}$ pound and the other weighs $\frac{3}{8}$ pound. What is the combined weight of both boxes?

   The combined weight is $\underline{1\frac{7}{40}}$ pounds.

8. In problem 7, how much more does the heavier box weigh?

   The heavier box weighs $\underline{\frac{23}{40}}$ pound more.

1.
2.
3.
4.
5.
6.
7.
8.

29

Lesson 21 Reciprocals

NAME _____

The product of any number and its **reciprocal** is 1.

$$\frac{2}{3} \times \frac{3}{2} = \frac{2 \times 3}{3 \times 2} = \frac{6}{6} = 1$$

The reciprocal of $\frac{2}{3}$ is $\frac{3}{2}$.

The reciprocal of $\frac{1}{2}$ is $\frac{2}{3}$.

reciprocals

$$\frac{1}{2} \times 2 = \frac{1}{2} \times \frac{2}{1} = \frac{2}{2} = 1$$

The reciprocal of $\frac{1}{2}$ is $\frac{2}{1}$ or 2.

The reciprocal of 2 is $\frac{1}{2}$.

Write the reciprocal of each of the following.

	a	b	c	d	e	f
1.	$\frac{3}{5}\ \frac{5}{3}$	$\frac{8}{7}\ \frac{7}{8}$	$\frac{5}{4}\ \frac{4}{5}$	$\frac{7}{5}\ \frac{5}{7}$	$\frac{9}{4}\ \frac{4}{9}$	$\frac{7}{6}\ \frac{6}{7}$
2.	$\frac{5}{3}\ \frac{3}{5}$	$\frac{9}{7}\ \frac{7}{8}$	$\frac{4}{5}\ \frac{5}{4}$	$\frac{5}{7}\ \frac{7}{5}$	$\frac{4}{9}\ \frac{9}{4}$	$\frac{6}{7}\ \frac{7}{6}$
3.	$\frac{1}{8}\ 8$	$\frac{1}{3}\ 3$	$\frac{1}{4}\ 4$	$\frac{1}{9}\ 9$	$\frac{1}{16}\ 16$	$\frac{1}{14}\ 14$
4.	$8\ \frac{1}{8}$	$3\ \frac{1}{3}$	$4\ \frac{1}{4}$	$9\ \frac{1}{9}$	$16\ \frac{1}{16}$	$14\ \frac{1}{14}$
5.	$8\ \frac{1}{8}$	$3\ \frac{1}{3}$	$4\ \frac{1}{4}$	$9\ \frac{1}{9}$	$16\ \frac{1}{16}$	$14\ \frac{1}{14}$
6.	$\frac{8}{5}\ \frac{5}{8}$	$6\ \frac{1}{6}$	$\frac{2}{3}\ \frac{3}{2}$	$\frac{6}{11}\ \frac{11}{6}$	$\frac{7}{4}\ \frac{4}{7}$	$12\ \frac{1}{12}$
7.	$15\ \frac{1}{15}$	$\frac{10}{9}\ \frac{9}{10}$	$\frac{12}{11}\ \frac{11}{12}$	$17\ \frac{1}{17}$	$\frac{9}{8}\ \frac{8}{9}$	$\frac{17}{12}\ \frac{12}{17}$
8.	$\frac{15}{8}\ \frac{8}{15}$	$\frac{5}{2}\ \frac{2}{5}$	$11\ \frac{1}{11}$	$\frac{7}{11}\ \frac{11}{7}$	$11\ \frac{1}{11}$	$\frac{17}{3}\ \frac{3}{17}$
9.	$\frac{10}{1}\ \frac{1}{10}$	$13\ \frac{1}{13}$	$\frac{1}{17}\ 17$	$\frac{11}{8}\ \frac{8}{11}$	$\frac{9}{7}\ \frac{7}{9}$	$5\ \frac{1}{5}$
10.	$\frac{5}{8}\ \frac{8}{5}$	$\frac{1}{6}\ 6$	$\frac{7}{7}\ \frac{7}{7}$	$\frac{12}{7}\ \frac{7}{12}$	$2\ \frac{1}{2}$	$\frac{5}{2}\ \frac{2}{5}$

30

Lesson 22 Division

NAME _____

$$15 \div \frac{3}{4} = \frac{15}{1} \times \frac{4}{3}$$
$$= \frac{15 \times 4}{1 \times 3}$$
$$= \frac{60}{3}$$
$$= 20$$

To divide by a fraction, multiply by its reciprocal.

Multiply the fractions.

Write the answer in simplest form.

$$10 \div \frac{6}{7} = \frac{10}{1} \times \frac{7}{6}$$
$$= \frac{10 \times 7}{1 \times 6}$$
$$= \frac{70}{6}$$
$$= 11\frac{2}{3}$$

Write each answer in simplest form.

	a	b	c	d
1.	$10 \div \frac{1}{3}\ 30$	$8 \div \frac{1}{2}\ 16$	$7 \div \frac{1}{4}\ 28$	$6 \div \frac{1}{5}\ 30$
2.	$14 \div \frac{2}{7}\ 49$	$15 \div \frac{2}{5}\ 37\frac{1}{2}$	$16 \div \frac{3}{8}\ 42\frac{2}{3}$	$18 \div \frac{5}{9}\ 32\frac{2}{5}$
3.	$18 \div \frac{1}{3}\ 54$	$14 \div \frac{7}{8}\ 16$	$17 \div \frac{1}{2}\ 34$	$12 \div \frac{3}{4}\ 16$

31

Lesson 23 Division

NAME _____

$$1\frac{1}{2} \div \frac{1}{3} = \frac{4}{3} \times \frac{3}{1}$$

Multiply by the reciprocal.

$$= \frac{1 \times 3}{3 \times 1}$$
$$= \frac{3}{4}$$

$$\frac{3}{4} \div \frac{1}{2} = \frac{3}{4} \times \frac{2}{1}$$
$$= \frac{3 \times 2}{4 \times 1}$$
$$= \frac{6}{4}$$
$$= 1\frac{2}{4}$$
$$= 1\frac{1}{2}$$

Multiply by the reciprocal.

Write the answer in simplest form.

Write each answer in simplest form.

	a	b	c	d
1.	$\frac{1}{5} \div \frac{1}{2}\ \frac{2}{5}$	$\frac{1}{3} \div \frac{1}{2}\ \frac{2}{3}$	$\frac{1}{8} \div \frac{1}{4}\ \frac{1}{2}$	$\frac{1}{9} \div \frac{1}{6}\ \frac{2}{3}$
2.	$\frac{3}{5} \div \frac{1}{2}\ 1\frac{1}{5}$	$\frac{4}{7} \div \frac{2}{3}\ \frac{6}{7}$	$\frac{4}{5} \div \frac{1}{10}\ 8$	$\frac{5}{6} \div \frac{2}{3}\ 1\frac{1}{4}$
3.	$\frac{4}{5} \div \frac{2}{7}\ 2$	$\frac{3}{8} \div \frac{3}{4}\ \frac{1}{2}$	$\frac{4}{9} \div \frac{1}{5}\ 2\frac{2}{9}$	$\frac{7}{8} \div \frac{7}{10}\ 1\frac{1}{4}$

32

69

ANSWER KEY

Problem Solving

Solve. Write each answer in simplest form. Use the space at the right to work each problem.

1. How many $\frac{1}{6}$-hour sessions are there in $\frac{1}{2}$ hour?
   There are 3 sessions.
2. Erika has a ribbon $\frac{3}{4}$ yard long. How many $\frac{1}{4}$-yard pieces can she get from her ribbon?
   She can get 3 pieces.
3. In problem 2, how many $\frac{1}{8}$-yard pieces can Erika get from her ribbon?
   She can get 6 pieces.
4. A machine uses gas at the rate of $\frac{1}{5}$ gallon an hour. So far $\frac{9}{10}$ gallon has been used. How many hours has the machine operated?
   The machine has operated $4\frac{1}{2}$ hours.
5. Suppose the machine in problem 4 has used $\frac{4}{5}$ gallon of gas. How many hours did the machine operate?
   The machine operated 4 hours.
6. Three-eighths pound of nuts is put in each bag. How many bags can be filled with $\frac{3}{4}$ pound of nuts?
   2 bags can be filled.
7. Jason walked $\frac{5}{8}$ hour. He walked at the rate of 1 mile every $\frac{1}{8}$ hour. How many miles did he walk?
   He walked 5 miles.
8. Suppose in problem 7 Jason walked 1 mile every $\frac{5}{16}$ hour. How many miles did he walk?
   He walked 2 miles.
9. A bell rings every $\frac{1}{6}$ hour. Assume it just rang. How many times will it ring in the next $\frac{2}{3}$ hour?
   It will ring 4 times.

33

NAME ____________

Lesson 24 Division

$2\frac{1}{5} \div 4 = \frac{11}{5} \div 4$ — Change the mixed numerals to fractions. — $3\frac{1}{2} \div 1\frac{1}{2} = \frac{7}{2} \div \frac{3}{2}$

$= \frac{11}{5} \times \frac{1}{4}$ — To divide, multiply by the reciprocal. — $= \frac{7}{2} \times \frac{2}{3}$

$= \frac{11}{20}$ — Multiply the fractions. — $= \frac{14}{6}$

Write the answer in simplest form. — $= 2\frac{1}{3}$

Write each answer in simplest form.

	a	b	c	d
1.	$2\frac{1}{2} \div 3$ $\frac{5}{6}$	$1\frac{2}{5} \div 3$ $\frac{7}{15}$	$4 \div 1\frac{1}{3}$ 3	$6 \div 1\frac{1}{3}$ $4\frac{1}{2}$
2.	$1\frac{2}{7} \div 2\frac{1}{2}$ $\frac{18}{35}$	$1\frac{1}{5} \div 2\frac{2}{3}$ $\frac{9}{20}$	$4\frac{1}{2} \div 1\frac{1}{5}$ $3\frac{3}{4}$	$1\frac{4}{5} \div 1\frac{1}{5}$ $1\frac{1}{2}$
3.	$1\frac{4}{5} \div \frac{2}{7}$ $6\frac{3}{10}$	$\frac{1}{6} \div 1\frac{1}{2}$ $\frac{1}{9}$	$3\frac{3}{5} \div 10$ $\frac{9}{25}$	$1\frac{1}{3} \div 2\frac{1}{2}$ $\frac{8}{15}$

34

NAME ____________

Lesson 25 Tenths

Numerals like 0.4, 4.1, and 5.4 are called decimals.

$\frac{1}{10} = 0.1$ — 0.1 is read "one tenth." — $0.4 = \frac{4}{10}$ — $\frac{3}{10} = 0.3$

decimal point

$4\frac{1}{10} = 4.1$ — 4.1 is read "four and one tenth." — $5.4 = 5\frac{4}{10}$ — $2\frac{3}{10} = 2.3$

Change each fraction or mixed numeral to a decimal.

	a	b	c	d
1.	$\frac{6}{10}$ = .6	$\frac{2}{10}$ = .2	$\frac{8}{10}$ = .8	$\frac{5}{10}$ = .5
2.	$4\frac{7}{10}$ = 4.7	$5\frac{9}{10}$ = 5.9	$18\frac{2}{10}$ = 18.2	$423\frac{6}{10}$ = 423.6

Change each decimal to a fraction or mixed numeral.

3.	0.7 = $\frac{7}{10}$	0.3 = $\frac{3}{10}$	0.1 = $\frac{1}{10}$	0.9 = $\frac{9}{10}$
4.	4.9 = $4\frac{9}{10}$	12.7 = $12\frac{7}{10}$	15.1 = $15\frac{1}{10}$	217.3 = $217\frac{3}{10}$

Write a decimal for each of the following.

	a		b	
5.	eight tenths	.8	three and seven tenths	3.7
6.	four tenths	.4	twenty-five and eight tenths	25.8
7.	five tenths	.5	one hundred and six tenths	100.6

Write each decimal in words.

8. 0.9 nine tenths
9. 3.7 three and seven tenths
10. 21.2 twenty-one and two tenths

35

NAME ____________

Lesson 26 Hundredths

$\frac{1}{100} = 0.01$ — 0.01 is read "one hundredth." — $0.15 = \frac{15}{100}$ — $\frac{9}{100} = 0.09$

$3\frac{12}{100} = 3.12$ — 3.12 is read "three and twelve hundredths." — $2.07 = 2\frac{7}{100}$ — $1\frac{14}{100} = 1.14$

Change each fraction or mixed numeral to a decimal naming hundredths.

	a	b	c
1.	$\frac{8}{100}$ = 0.08	$\frac{16}{100}$ = 0.16	$\frac{5}{100}$ = 0.05
2.	$1\frac{36}{100}$ = 1.36	$8\frac{6}{100}$ = 8.06	$9\frac{12}{100}$ = 9.12
3.	$12\frac{45}{100}$ = 12.45	$43\frac{67}{100}$ = 43.67	$26\frac{4}{100}$ = 26.04
4.	$142\frac{8}{100}$ = 142.08	$436\frac{42}{100}$ = 436.42	$389\frac{89}{100}$ = 389.89

Change each decimal to a fraction or mixed numeral.

5.	0.17 = $\frac{17}{100}$	0.03 = $\frac{3}{100}$	0.41 = $\frac{41}{100}$
6.	5.19 = $5\frac{19}{100}$	6.47 = $6\frac{47}{100}$	5.01 = $5\frac{1}{100}$
7.	21.07 = $21\frac{7}{100}$	23.99 = $23\frac{99}{100}$	44.89 = $44\frac{89}{100}$
8.	142.33 = $142\frac{33}{100}$	483.03 = $483\frac{3}{100}$	185.63 = $185\frac{63}{100}$

Write a decimal for each of the following.

	a		b	
9.	eight hundredths	0.08	six and twenty-three hundredths	6.23
10.	ninety-five hundredths	0.95	fourteen and sixty hundredths	14.60
11.	forty-eight hundredths	0.48	four and forty-four hundredths	4.44

36

NAME ____________

Lesson 27 Thousandths, Ten-Thousandths

$\frac{1}{1000} = 0.001$ ← one thousandth — $\frac{1}{10000} = 0.0001$ ← one ten-thousandth

$2\frac{12}{1000} = 2.012$ ← two and twelve thousandths — $1\frac{35}{10000} = 1.0035$ ← one and thirty-five ten-thousandths

Write each fraction or mixed numeral as a decimal.

	a	b	c
1.	$\frac{8}{1000}$ = 0.008	$\frac{17}{1000}$ = 0.017	$\frac{54}{10000}$ = 0.0054
2.	$\frac{125}{10000}$ = 0.0125	$\frac{430}{1000}$ = 0.430	$\frac{306}{10000}$ = 0.0306
3.	$4\frac{4}{1000}$ = 4.004	$3\frac{41}{10000}$ = 3.0041	$6\frac{183}{1000}$ = 6.183
4.	$35\frac{78}{10000}$ = 35.0078	$42\frac{19}{1000}$ = 42.019	$196\frac{6}{1000}$ = 196.006

Write each decimal as a fraction or as a mixed numeral.

	a	b	c
5.	0.009 = $\frac{9}{1000}$	0.0019 = $\frac{19}{10000}$	0.0003 = $\frac{3}{10000}$
6.	0.123 = $\frac{123}{1000}$	0.0441 = $\frac{441}{10000}$	0.219 = $\frac{219}{1000}$
7.	4.011 = $4\frac{11}{1000}$	2.1011 = $2\frac{1011}{10000}$	6.0014 = $6\frac{14}{10000}$
8.	36.037 = $36\frac{37}{1000}$	3.433 = $3\frac{433}{1000}$	100.0001 = $100\frac{1}{10000}$

Write a decimal for each of the following.

	a		b	
9.	fifty-three thousandths	0.053	ten and nine ten-thousandths	10.0009
10.	eleven ten-thousandths	0.0011	twelve and eighteen thousandths	12.018
11.	sixty-five thousandths	0.065	twelve and one thousandth	12.001

37

NAME ____________

Lesson 28 Fractions to Decimals

Change $\frac{1}{2}$ to tenths.
$\frac{1}{2} = \frac{1}{2} \times \frac{5}{5}$
$= \frac{5}{10}$
$= 0.5$

Change $\frac{1}{2}$ to hundredths.
$\frac{1}{2} = \frac{1}{2} \times \frac{50}{50}$
$= \frac{50}{100}$
$= 0.50$

Change $\frac{1}{2}$ to thousandths.
$\frac{1}{2} = \frac{1}{2} \times \frac{500}{500}$
$= \frac{500}{1000}$
$= 0.500$

Change $\frac{3}{4}$ to hundredths.
$\frac{3}{4} = \frac{3}{4} \times \frac{25}{25}$
$= \frac{75}{100}$
$= .75$

Change $3\frac{48}{250}$ to thousandths.
$3\frac{48}{250} = 3 + \frac{48}{250}$
$= 3 + (\frac{48}{250} \times \frac{4}{4})$
$= 3 + \frac{192}{1000}$
$= 3\frac{192}{1000}$
$= 3.192$

Change each of the following to a decimal as indicated.

	a	b	c
1.	Change $\frac{3}{5}$ to tenths. 0.6	Change $\frac{3}{5}$ to hundredths. 0.60	Change $\frac{3}{5}$ to thousandths. 0.600
2.	Change $3\frac{1}{2}$ to tenths. 3.5	Change $\frac{7}{25}$ to hundredths. 0.28	Change $2\frac{19}{100}$ to thousandths. 2.190
3.	Change $2\frac{4}{5}$ to tenths. 2.8	Change $\frac{7}{20}$ to hundredths. 0.35	Change $\frac{7}{125}$ to thousandths. 0.056
4.	Change $2\frac{1}{5}$ to tenths. 2.2	Change $\frac{19}{50}$ to hundredths. 0.38	Change $\frac{88}{250}$ to thousandths. 0.352

38

ANSWER KEY

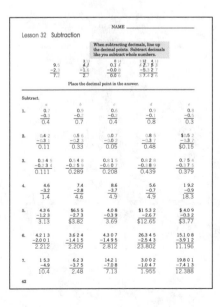
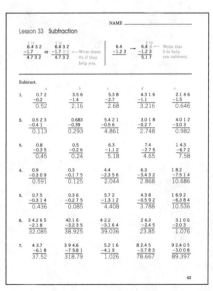
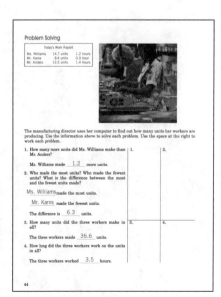

Lesson 29 Decimals to Fractions

$0.7 = \frac{7}{10}$ $0.6 = \frac{6}{10}$ or $\frac{3}{5}$ $4.2 = 4\frac{2}{10}$ or $4\frac{1}{5}$

$0.19 = \frac{19}{100}$ $0.14 = \frac{14}{100}$ or $\frac{7}{50}$ $3.01 = 3\frac{1}{100}$

$0.051 = \frac{51}{1000}$ $0.114 = \frac{114}{1000}$ or $\frac{57}{500}$ $5.006 = 5\frac{6}{1000}$ or $5\frac{3}{500}$

Change each decimal to a fraction or mixed numeral in simplest form.

	a	b	c	d
1.	$0.3\ \frac{3}{10}$	$0.1\ \frac{1}{10}$	$0.4\ \frac{2}{5}$	$0.5\ \frac{1}{2}$
2.	$2.7\ 2\frac{7}{10}$	$3.3\ 3\frac{3}{10}$	$7.2\ 7\frac{1}{5}$	$5.8\ 5\frac{4}{5}$
3.	$0.17\ \frac{17}{100}$	$0.03\ \frac{3}{100}$	$0.15\ \frac{3}{20}$	$0.80\ \frac{4}{5}$
4.	$5.07\ 5\frac{7}{100}$	$8.43\ 8\frac{43}{100}$	$4.05\ 4\frac{1}{20}$	$2.44\ 2\frac{11}{25}$
5.	$0.003\ \frac{3}{1000}$	$0.017\ \frac{17}{1000}$	$0.125\ \frac{1}{8}$	$0.045\ \frac{9}{200}$
6.	$3.121\ 3\frac{121}{1000}$	$2.987\ 2\frac{987}{1000}$	$4.250\ 4\frac{1}{4}$	$3.008\ 3\frac{1}{125}$
7.	$4.35\ 4\frac{7}{20}$	$0.7\ \frac{7}{10}$	$6.200\ 6\frac{1}{5}$	$1.007\ 1\frac{7}{1000}$
8.	$2.6\ 2\frac{3}{5}$	$3.24\ 3\frac{6}{25}$	$0.250\ \frac{1}{4}$	$3.5\ 3\frac{1}{2}$
9.	$5.125\ 5\frac{1}{8}$	$0.9\ \frac{9}{10}$	$2.4\ 2\frac{2}{5}$	$0.04\ \frac{1}{25}$
10.	$0.01\ \frac{1}{100}$	$0.051\ \frac{51}{1000}$	$0.8\ \frac{4}{5}$	$2.19\ 2\frac{19}{100}$

39

Lesson 30 Addition

When adding decimals, line up the decimal points. Add decimals like you add whole numbers.

```
   0.6          3.5 6         3.0 1 8
  +0.7          0.3           0.1 4 2
  ─────        +4.2 4       +1 4.0 0 9
   1.3          7.8 3        1 7.1 6 9
```
← Place the decimal point in the answer.

Add.

	a	b	c	d	e
1.	0.4 +0.5 = **0.9**	0.9 +0.8 = **1.7**	3.4 +9.2 = **12.6**	19.3 +12.8 = **32.1**	45.6 +6.8 = **52.4**
2.	$0.4\ 2$ +0.3 5 = **0.77**	$0.7\ 6$ +0.4 8 = **1.24**	$3.3\ 2$ +4.6 2 = **7.94**	$24.4\ 5$ +72.3 6 = **96.81**	$58.9\ 2$ +3.2 9 = **62.21**
3.	$0.01\ 4$ +0.2 3 1 = **0.245**	$0.45\ 6$ +0.8 7 6 = **1.332**	$2.01\ 4$ +2.3 2 5 = **4.339**	$3.45\ 7$ +2.3 5 6 = **5.813**	$41.21\ 6$ +2.0 0 7 = **43.223**
4.	0.5 0.6 +0.7 = **1.8**	1.9 2.2 +3.4 = **7.5**	3.4 1.7 +4.8 = **9.9**	$4.2\ 3$ 1.6 +2.9 = **46.8**	3.4 0.8 +4.2 = **8.4**
5.	$0.3\ 3$ 0.2 6 +0.4 1 = **1.00**	$\$0.4\ 3$ 0.5 4 +0.0 7 = **$1.04**	$3.3\ 5$ 1.0 8 +6.1 1 = **10.54**	$\$24.2\ 9$ 12.2 9 +5.3 1 = **$41.89**	$\$3.4\ 0\ 5$ 2.0 6 +1.0 8 = **$37.19**
6.	$0.0\ 1\ 2$ 0.3 0 4 +0.4 0 5 = **0.721**	$0.4\ 2\ 3$ 0.0 5 6 +0.2 1 7 = **0.696**	$3.0\ 5\ 6$ 1.4 5 2 +6.1 1 2 = **10.620**	$4.0\ 0\ 8$ 2.3 0 9 +0.0 1 2 = **6.329**	$3.5\ 1\ 5\ 7$ 0.4 4 8 +2.5 0 9 = **38.114**

40

Lesson 31 Addition

You may write these 0's if they help you add.

```
  0.8           0.8          4.2           4.2 0 0
 +0.3 9  or   +0.3 9       3.0 1 8   or   3.0 1 8
  ─────        ─────       0.8 2         0.8 2 0
  1.1 9        1.1 9      +8.0 3 8      +8.0 3 8
                           8.0 3 8       8.0 3 8
```

Add. If necessary, use 0's as shown in the examples.

	a	b	c	d	e
1.	0.9 +0.4 = **1.32**	$0.8\ 3$ +0.4 = **1.23**	0.6 +0.4 0 1 = **1.001**	$0.7\ 2$ +0.4 2 3 = **1.143**	$0.6\ 4\ 5$ +0.2 = **0.845**
2.	$2.7\ 5$ +3.3 0 8 = **6.058**	$5.5\ 4$ +7.6 = **13.14**	3.8 +0.3 1 6 = **4.116**	$0.2\ 9$ +8.0 4 3 = **8.333**	$2\ 9.5$ +4.9 3 = **34.43**
3.	$0.4\ 2$ 0.8 +0.0 1 8 = **1.238**	$0.3\ 1$ 0.2 +0.4 5 = **0.96**	$0.7\ 6$ 0.8 2 +0.9 = **2.48**	$0.4\ 3\ 1$ 0.2 +0.4 5 = **1.081**	0.5 0.3 1 6 +0.0 9 9 = **0.915**
4.	$3.1\ 8\ 2$ 1.3 4 +2.6 = **7.122**	$4.7\ 2$ 5.8 +6.3 1 7 = **16.837**	$7.4\ 2\ 6$ 3.3 1 8 +0.2 = **10.944**	$0.7\ 3\ 1$ 8.4 5 +2.2 8 = **11.461**	0.3 0.3 8 4 +9.4 2 = **10.104**

Complete the following.

	a	b
5.	0.8 + 0.91 = **1.71**	0.4 + 0.016 + 0.75 = **1.166**
6.	0.58 + 0.114 = **0.694**	0.32 + 0.42 + 0.113 = **0.853**
7.	0.9 + 0.301 = **1.201**	4.8 + 3.21 + 0.014 = **8.024**
8.	2.4 + 0.31 = **2.71**	5.24 + 0.016 + 21.3 = **26.556**

41

Lesson 32 Subtraction

When subtracting decimals, line up the decimal points. Subtract decimals like you subtract whole numbers.

```
  9.5          4.4          0.1 4          0.1 0           3.7 0 6
 -2.3         -1.6         -0.0 8         -0.0 6          -5.3 2 7
 ─────        ─────        ──────         ──────          ───────
  7.2          2.7          0.0 6          0.0 6           3.7 4 2 6
```
← Place the decimal point in the answer.

Subtract.

	a	b	c	d	e
1.	0.7 -0.3 = **0.4**	0.9 -0.2 = **0.7**	0.6 -0.2 = **0.4**	0.9 -0.1 = **0.8**	0.8 -0.5 = **0.3**
2.	$0.4\ 2$ -0.3 1 = **0.11**	$0.5\ 6$ -0.2 3 = **0.33**	$0.0\ 7$ -0.0 2 = **0.05**	$0.8\ 5$ -0.3 7 = **0.48**	$\$0.5\ 2$ -0.3 7 = **$0.15**
3.	$0.3\ 4\ 5$ -0.2 3 4 = **0.111**	$0.5\ 4\ 8$ -0.2 5 9 = **0.289**	$0.8\ 1\ 5$ -0.6 0 7 = **0.208**	$0.8\ 2\ 8$ -0.3 8 9 = **0.439**	$0.7\ 5\ 4$ -0.3 7 5 = **0.379**
4.	4.6 -3.2 = **1.4**	7.4 -2.8 = **4.6**	8.6 -3.7 = **4.9**	5.6 -0.7 = **4.9**	$1\ 9.2$ -0.9 = **18.3**
5.	$4.3\ 6$ -1.2 3 = **3.13**	$\$6.5\ 5$ -2.7 3 = **$3.82**	$4.0\ 8$ -0.3 9 = **3.69**	$\$1\ 5.3\ 2$ -2.6 7 = **$12.65**	$\$4.0\ 9$ -0.3 2 = **$3.77**
6.	$4.2\ 1\ 3$ -2.0 0 1 = **2.212**	$3.6\ 2\ 4$ -1.4 1 5 = **2.209**	$4.3\ 0\ 7$ -1.4 9 5 = **2.812**	$26.3\ 4\ 5$ -2.5 4 3 = **23.802**	$15.1\ 0\ 8$ -3.9 1 2 = **11.196**
7.	$1\ 5.3$ -4.9 = **10.4**	$6.2\ 3$ -3.7 5 = **2.48**	$14.2\ 1$ -7.0 8 = **7.13**	$3.0\ 0\ 2$ -1.0 4 7 = **1.955**	$19.8\ 0\ 1$ -7.4 1 3 = **12.388**

42

Lesson 33 Subtraction

```
  6.4 3 2          6.4 3 2            6.4          6.4
 -1.7     or      -1.7 0 0          -1.2 3  →    -1.2 3
 ───────          ───────          ──────       ──────
  4.7 3 2          4.7 3 2                         5.1 7
```
← Write these 0's if they help you.   Write this 0 to help you subtract.

Subtract.

	a	b	c	d	e
1.	$0.7\ 2$ -0.2 = **0.52**	$3.5\ 6$ -1.4 = **2.16**	$5.3\ 8$ -2.7 = **2.68**	$4.3\ 1\ 6$ -1.1 = **3.216**	$2.1\ 4\ 6$ -1.5 = **0.646**
2.	$0.5\ 2\ 3$ -0.4 1 = **0.113**	$0.6\ 8\ 3$ -0.3 9 = **0.293**	$5.4\ 2\ 1$ -0.5 6 = **4.861**	$3.0\ 1\ 8$ -0.2 7 = **2.748**	$4.0\ 1\ 2$ -3.0 3 = **0.982**
3.	0.8 -0.3 5 = **0.45**	0.5 -0.2 6 = **0.24**	6.3 -1.1 2 = **5.18**	7.4 -2.7 5 = **4.65**	$1\ 4.3$ -6.7 2 = **7.58**
4.	0.9 -0.3 0 9 = **0.591**	0.3 -0.1 7 5 = **0.125**	4.4 -2.3 5 6 = **2.044**	6.3 -3.4 3 2 = **2.868**	$1\ 8.2$ -7.5 1 4 = **10.686**
5.	$0.7\ 5$ -0.3 1 4 = **0.436**	$0.3\ 6$ -0.2 7 5 = **0.085**	$5.7\ 2$ -1.3 1 2 = **4.408**	$4.3\ 8$ -0.5 9 2 = **3.788**	$1\ 6.9\ 2$ -6.3 8 4 = **10.536**
6.	$3\ 4.2\ 6\ 5$ -2.1 8 = **32.085**	$42.1\ 6$ -3.2 3 5 = **38.925**	$4.2\ 2$ -3.1 6 4 = **39.036**	$2\ 6.3$ -2.4 5 = **23.85**	$3.1\ 0\ 6$ -2.0 3 = **1.076**
7.	$4\ 3.7$ -6.1 8 = **37.52**	$3\ 9\ 4.6$ -7 5.8 1 = **318.79**	$5.2\ 1\ 6$ -4.1 9 = **1.026**	$8\ 2\ 4.5$ -3.7 8 3 = **78.667**	$9\ 2\ 4.0\ 5$ -3 0.0 8 = **89.397**

43

Problem Solving

Today's Work Report

Ms. Williams	14.7 units	1.2 hours
Mr. Karns	8.4 units	0.9 hour
Mr. Anders	13.5 units	1.4 hours

The manufacturing director uses her computer to find out how many units her workers are producing. Use the information above to solve each problem. Use the space at the right to work each problem.

1. How many more units did Ms. Williams make than Mr. Anders?

   Ms. Williams made **1.2** more units.

2. Who made the most units? Who made the fewest units? What is the difference between the most and the fewest units made?

   Ms. Williams made the most units.

   Mr. Karns made the fewest units.

   The difference is **6.3** units.

3. How many units did the three workers make in all?

   The three workers made **36.6** units.

4. How long did the three workers work on the units in all?

   The three workers worked **3.5** hours.

44

ANSWER KEY

Lesson 34 Multiplication

number of digits to the right of the decimal point

4 ×3 = 12 (0)	0.4 ×3 = 1.2 (1)	0.04 ×3 = 0.12 (2)	0.04 ×.3 = 0.012 (3)	0.04 ×.03 = 0.0012 (4)

Write in as many 0's as needed to place the decimal point correctly.

Multiply.

	a	b	c	d	e
1.	2 ×3 = 6	0.2 ×3 = 0.6	0.02 ×3 = 0.06	0.002 ×3 = 0.006	2 ×0.3 = 0.6
2.	8 ×6 = 48	0.8 ×6 = 4.8	0.08 ×6 = 0.48	0.008 ×6 = 0.048	0.6 ×8 = 0.48
3.	5 ×3 = 15	0.5 ×3 = 1.5	0.05 ×3 = 0.15	0.005 ×3 = 0.015	0.003 ×5 = 0.015
4.	3 ×4 = 12	0.3 ×0.4 = 0.12	0.03 ×0.4 = 0.012	0.04 ×0.3 = 0.012	0.03 ×0.04 = 0.0012
5.	6 ×7 = 42	0.6 ×0.7 = 0.42	0.06 ×0.7 = 0.042	0.06 ×0.7 = 0.042	0.06 ×0.07 = 0.0042
6.	9 ×8 = 72	0.9 ×0.8 = 0.72	0.09 ×0.8 = 0.072	0.08 ×0.9 = 0.072	0.09 ×0.08 = 0.0072

45

Lesson 35 Multiplication

number of digits to the right of the decimal point

24 ×36 = 864 (0)	2.4 ×36 = 86.4 (1)	0.24 ×36 = 8.64 (2)	0.24 ×3.6 = 0.864 (3)	0.24 ×.36 = 0.0864 (4)

Use the completed multiplication to find each product.

	a	b	c	d
1.	32 ×14 = 448	3.2 ×14 = 44.8	0.32 ×14 = 4.48	0.32 ×1.4 = 0.448 / 0.32 ×0.14 = 0.0448
2.	27 ×48 = 1,296	2.7 ×48 = 129.6	0.27 ×48 = 12.96	0.27 ×4.8 = 1.296 / 0.27 ×0.48 = 0.1296
3.	26 ×34 = 884	0.26 ×34 = 8.84	0.26 ×3.4 = 0.884	0.26 ×0.34 = 0.0884 / 2.6 ×34 = 88.4
4.	74 ×26 = 1,924	0.74 ×2.6 = 1.924	7.4 ×26 = 192.4	0.74 ×26 = 19.24 / 0.74 ×0.26 = 0.1924
5.	25 ×3 = 75	25 ×0.3 = 7.5	0.25 ×0.3 = 0.075	25 ×0.03 = 0.75 / 0.25 ×0.03 = 0.0075
6.	12 ×4 = 48	1.2 ×0.4 = 0.48	0.12 ×4 = 0.48	0.12 ×0.4 = 0.048 / 0.12 ×0.04 = 0.0048
7.	73 ×3 = 219	73 ×0.03 = 2.19	0.73 ×0.03 = 0.0219	7.3 ×0.3 = 2.19 / 0.73 ×0.3 = 0.219

46

Lesson 36 Multiplication

2.51 ×10 = 25.10 or 25.1	2.51 ×100 = 251.00 or 251	2.51 ×1000 = 2510.00 or 2,510

Shortcut
2.51 × 10 = 2.5,1
2.51 × 100 = 2,51.
2.51 × 1000 = 2,510.

0.085 ×10 = 0.850 or 0.85	0.085 ×100 = 8.500 or 8.5	0.085 ×1000 = 85.000 or 85

0.085 × 10 = 0.85
0.085 × 100 = 08.5
0.085 × 1000 = 085.

Multiply.

	a	b	c	d	e
1.	5.642 ×10 = 56.42	5.642 ×100 = 564.2	5.642 ×1000 = 5642	5.642 ×1000 = 5642	0.5642 ×10 = 5.642
2.	0.1064 ×10 = 1.064	0.1064 ×100 = 10.64	0.1064 ×1000 = 106.4	0.0106 ×10 = 0.106	1.064 ×1000 = 1064
3.	0.23 ×10 = 2.3	0.23 ×100 = 23	0.23 ×1000 = 230	0.023 ×10 = 0.23	0.0023 ×100 = 0.23
4.	0.008 ×10 = 0.08	0.008 ×100 = 0.8	0.008 ×1000 = 8	0.08 ×100 = 8	0.08 ×1000 = 80
5.	1.5 ×10 = 15	1.5 ×100 = 150	1.5 ×1000 = 1500	1.5 ×1000 = 1500	0.15 ×10 = 1.5

47

Lesson 37 Division

Place a decimal point in the quotient directly above the decimal point in the dividend. Then divide as if both numbers were whole numbers.

6)102 = 17	6)10.2 = 1.7	6)1.02 = 0.17	6)0.102 = 0.017

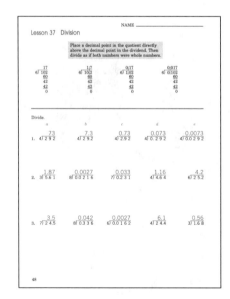

Divide.

	a	b	c	d	e
1.	4)29.2 = 7.3	4)29.2 = 7.3	4)2.92 = 0.73	4)0.292 = 0.073	4)0.0292 = 0.0073
2.	3)5.61 = 1.87	8)0.0216 = 0.0027	7)0.231 = 0.033	4)4.64 = 1.16	6)25.2 = 4.2
3.	7)24.5 = 3.5	8)0.336 = 0.042	6)0.0162 = 0.0027	4)24.4 = 6.1	3)1.68 = 0.56

48

Lesson 38 Division

Multiply the divisor and the dividend by 10, by 100, or by 1000 so the new divisor is a whole number.

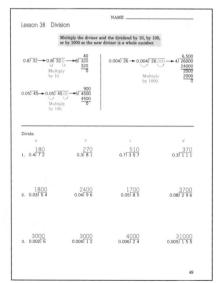

Divide.

	a	b	c	d
1.	0.4)72 = 180	0.3)81 = 270	0.7)357 = 510	0.3)111 = 370
2.	0.03)54 = 1800	0.04)96 = 2400	0.05)85 = 1700	0.08)296 = 3700
3.	0.002)6 = 3000	0.004)12 = 3000	0.006)24 = 4000	0.005)155 = 31000

49

Lesson 39 Division

0.5)11.5 → 0.5)11.5 → 5)115 = 23 (Multiply by 10)	0.06)0.426 → 0.06)0.426 → 6)42.6 = 7.1 (Multiply by 100)

0.003)2.1 → 0.003)2.100 → 3)2100 = 700 (Multiply by 1,000)

Divide.

	a	b	c	d
1.	0.4)7.2 = 18	0.3)0.81 = 2.7	0.8)0.392 = 49	0.6)55.2 = 92
2.	0.06)0.84 = 14	0.04)0.068 = 1.7	0.08)0.224 = 2.8	0.07)2.52 = 36
3.	0.002)0.008 = 4	0.007)0.0042 = 6	0.008)0.144 = 18	0.009)0.0333 = 3.7
4.	0.004)0.096 = 24	0.09)6.3 = 70	0.006)0.009 = 1.5	0.7)8.4 = 12

50

ANSWER KEY

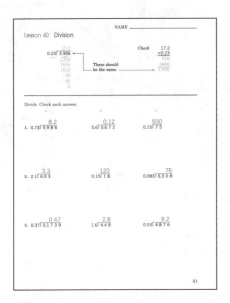

NAME _____

Lesson 40   Division

```
          17.2
0.23) 3.956              Check    17.2
      2300                       ×0.23
      1656      These should      516
      1610      be the same.     3440
        46                       3.956
        46
         0
```

Divide. Check each answer.

	a	b	c
1.	0.73) 5.9 8 6 = 8.2	5.6) 0.6 7 2 = 0.12	0.15) 7 5 = 500
2.	2.1) 6.9 3 = 3.3	0.15) 1 8 = 120	0.083) 6.3 0 8 = 76
3.	0.37) 0.1 7 3 9 = 0.47	1.6) 4.4 8 = 2.8	0.53) 4.8 7 6 = 9.2

51

NAME _____

Lesson 41   Length

1 foot (ft) = 12 inches (in.)	1 in. = 1/12 ft
1 yard (yd) = 3 ft	1 ft = 1/3 yd
1 yd = 36 in.	1 in. = 1/36 yd
1 mile (mi) = 5,280 ft	1 mi = 1,760 yd

36 in. = ___?___ ft   6 ft 4 in. = ___?___ in.

(36 × 1) in. = (36 × 1/12) ft   6 ft = 12 in.

36 in. = __3__ ft   6 ft = (6 × 12) or 72 in.

                             6 ft 4 in. = (72 + 4) in.

                             6 ft 4 in. = __76__ in.

Complete the following.

	a		b
1. 6 ft = __72__ in.		60 in. = __5__ ft
2. 9 yd = __27__ ft		12 ft = __4__ yd
3. 5 yd = __180__ in.		144 in. = __4__ yd
4. 3 mi = __15840__ ft		3 mi = __5280__ yd
5. 5 yd = __15__ ft		18 in. = __1 1/2__
6. 2 mi = __10560__ ft		5 mi = __8800__ yd
7. 5 ft 4 in. = __64__ in.		
8. 3 yd 5 in. = __113__ in.		
9. 5 yd 2 ft = __17__ ft		
10. 9 ft 6 in. = __114__ in.		
11. 1 mi 750 ft = __6030__ ft		

52

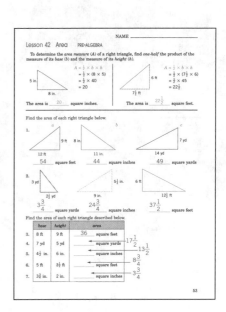

NAME _____

Lesson 42   Area   PRE-ALGEBRA

To determine the *area measure* (A) of a right triangle, find *one-half* the product of the measure of its *base* (b) and the measure of its *height* (h).

$A = \frac{1}{2} \times b \times h$ $A = \frac{1}{2} \times b \times h$
$= \frac{1}{2} \times (8 \times 5)$ $= \frac{1}{2} \times (7\frac{1}{2} \times 6)$
$= \frac{1}{2} \times 40$ $= \frac{1}{2} \times 45$
$= 20$ $= 22\frac{1}{2}$

The area is __20__ square inches.   The area is __22 1/2__ square feet.

Find the area of each right triangle below.

	a	b	c
1.	9 ft, 12 ft → __54__ square feet	8 in., 11 in. → __44__ square inches	14 yd, 7 yd → __49__ square yards
2.	3 yd, 2 1/2 yd → __3 3/4__ square yards	9 in., 5 1/2 in. → __24 3/4__ square inches	6 ft, 12 1/2 ft → __37 1/2__ square feet

Find the area of each right triangle described below.

	base	height	area
3.	8 ft	9 ft	__36__ square feet
4.	7 yd	5 yd	__17 1/2__ square yards
5.	4 1/2 in.	6 in.	__13 1/2__ square inches
6.	5 ft	3 1/2 ft	__8 3/4__ square feet
7.	3 3/4 in.	2 in.	__3 3/4__ square inches

53

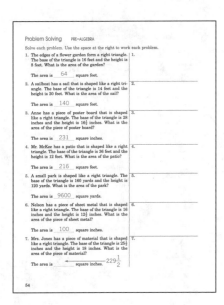

Problem Solving   PRE-ALGEBRA

Solve each problem. Use the space at the right to work each problem.

1. The edges of a flower garden form a right triangle. The base of the triangle is 16 feet and the height is 8 feet. What is the area of the garden?

   The area is __64__ square feet.

2. A sailboat has a sail that is shaped like a right triangle. The base of the triangle is 14 feet and the height is 20 feet. What is the area of the sail?

   The area is __140__ square feet.

3. Anne has a piece of poster board that is shaped like a right triangle. The base of the triangle is 28 inches and the height is 16 1/2 inches. What is the area of the piece of poster board?

   The area is __231__ square inches.

4. Mr. McKee has a patio that is shaped like a right triangle. The base of the triangle is 36 feet and the height is 12 feet. What is the area of the patio?

   The area is __216__ square feet.

5. A small park is shaped like a right triangle. The base of the triangle is 160 yards and the height is 120 yards. What is the area of the park?

   The area is __9600__ square yards.

6. Nelson has a piece of sheet metal that is shaped like a right triangle. The base of the triangle is 16 inches and the height is 12 1/2 inches. What is the area of the sheet metal?

   The area is __100__ square inches.

7. Mrs. Jones has a piece of material that is shaped like a right triangle. The base of the triangle is 25 1/2 inches and the height is 18 inches. What is the area of the piece of material?

   The area is __229 1/2__ square inches.

54

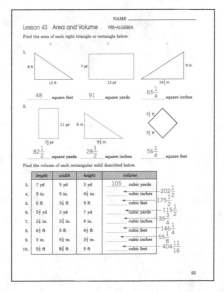

NAME _____

Lesson 43   Area and Volume   PRE-ALGEBRA

Find the area of each right triangle or rectangle below.

	a	b	c
1.	8 in., 12 in. → __48__ square feet	7 yd, 13 yd → __91__ square yards	9 in., 14 1/2 in. → __65 1/4__ square inches
2.	11 yd, 7 1/2 yd → __82 1/2__ square yards	6 in., 9 1/2 in. → __28 1/2__ square inches	7 1/2 ft → __56 1/4__ square feet

Find the volume of each rectangular solid described below.

	length	width	height	volume
3.	7 yd	5 yd	3 yd	__105__ cubic yards
4.	9 in.	5 in.	4 1/2 in.	__202 1/2__ cubic inches
5.	6 ft	3 1/2 ft	9 ft	__175 1/2__ cubic feet
6.	7 1/2 yd	3 yd	2 yd	__115 1/2__ cubic yards
7.	3 1/2 in.	2 1/2 in.	4 in.	__35 3/4__ cubic inches
8.	6 1/2 ft	5 ft	4 1/2 ft	__146 1/4__ cubic feet
9.	3 in.	5 1/2 in.	3 1/2 in.	__55 1/8__ cubic inches
10.	9 1/2 ft	8 1/2 ft	5 ft	__404 11/16__ cubic feet

55

Problem Solving   PRE-ALGEBRA

Solve each problem. Use the space at the right to work each problem.

1. A basketball court is shaped like a rectangle. The length is 84 feet and the width is 50 feet. What is the area of the court?

   The area is __4200__ square feet.

2. A garden plot is shaped like a right triangle. The base of the triangle is 50 feet and the height is 18 feet. What is the area of the triangle?

   The area is __450__ square feet.

3. A suitcase is 32 inches long, 16 inches wide, and 6 inches deep. What is the volume of the suitcase?

   The volume is __3072__ cubic inches.

4. Mrs. Langley has a flower bed that is shaped like a right triangle. The base of the triangle is 12 1/2 feet and the height is 6 feet. What is the area of the flower bed?

   The area is __37 1/2__ square feet.

5. A plot of land is shaped like a rectangle. It is 280 yards long and 90 yards wide. What is the area of the plot?

   The area is __25200__ square yards.

6. A box is 9 inches long, 6 1/2 inches wide, and 1 1/2 inches deep. What is the volume of the box?

   The volume is __87 3/4__ cubic inches.

7. A rectangular tabletop is 72 inches long and 36 inches wide. What is the area of the tabletop?

   The area is __2592__ square inches.

8. A brick is 8 inches long, 3 inches wide, and 2 inches high. How much space does the brick occupy?

   The brick occupies __48__ cubic inches of space.

56

73

Answer Key

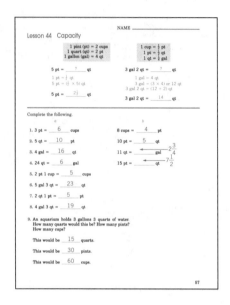

Lesson 44 Capacity

1 pint (pt) = 2 cups	1 cup = ½ pt
1 quart (qt) = 2 pt	1 pt = ½ qt
1 gallon (gal) = 4 qt	1 qt = ¼ gal

5 pt = __?__ qt   3 gal 2 qt = __?__ qt

1 pt = ½ qt   1 gal = 4 qt
5 pt = 1½ × 5½ qt   3 gal = (3 × 4) or 12 qt
                         3 gal 2 qt = (12 + 2) qt

5 pt = 2½ qt   3 gal 2 qt = __14__ qt

Complete the following.

	a	b
1.	3 pt = __6__ cups	8 cups = __4__ pt
2.	5 qt = __10__ pt	10 pt = __5__ qt
3.	4 gal = __16__ qt	11 qt = __2¾__ gal
4.	24 qt = __6__ gal	15 pt = __7½__ qt
5.	2 pt 1 cup = __5__ cups	
6.	5 gal 3 qt = __23__ qt	
7.	2 qt 1 pt = __5__ pt	
8.	4 gal 3 qt = __19__ qt	

9. An aquarium holds 3 gallons 3 quarts of water. How many quarts would this be? How many pints? How many cups?

This would be __15__ quarts.

This would be __30__ pints.

This would be __60__ cups.

57

Lesson 45 Weight and Time

| 1 pound (lb) = 16 ounces (oz) | 1 oz = 1/16 lb |
| 1 ton = 2,000 lb | |

1 minute (min) = 60 seconds (sec)	1 sec = 1/60 min
1 hour = 60 min	1 min = 1/60 hour
1 day = 24 hours	1 hour = 1/24 day

80 oz = __?__ lb   1 min 12 sec = __?__ sec

1 oz = 1/16 lb   1 min = 60 sec
80 oz = (80 × 1/16) lb   1 min 12 sec = (60 + 12) sec

80 oz = __5__ lb   1 min 12 sec = __72__ sec

Complete the following.

	a	b
1.	72 lb = __1152__ oz	80 oz = __5__ lb
2.	4 tons = __8000__ lb	6,000 lb = __3__ tons
3.	3 min = __180__ sec	120 sec = __2__ min
4.	5 hours = __300__ min	360 min = __6__ hours
5.	5 days = __120__ hours	144 hours = __6__ days
6.	3 lb 12 oz = __60__ oz	5 lb 6 oz = __86__ oz
7.	3 tons 500 lb = __6500__ lb	
8.	2 hr 45 min = __165__ min	
9.	4 days 12 hours = __108__ hours	
10.	4 hours 20 min = __260__ min	
11.	2 days 8 hours = __56__ hours	

58

Lesson 46 Percent

The symbol % (read **percent**) means 1/100 or 0.01.

3% = 3 × 1/100 or 3% = 3 × 0.01   17% = 17 × 1/100 or 17% = 17 × 0.01

= 3/100   = 0.03   = 17/100   = 0.17

Complete the following.

	percent	fraction	decimal
1.	1%	1/100	0.01
2.	7%	7/100	0.07
3.	29%	29/100	0.29
4.	47%	47/100	0.47
5.	53%	53/100	0.53
6.	21%	21/100	0.21
7.	83%	83/100	0.83
8.	49%	49/100	0.49
9.	61%	61/100	0.61
10.	9%	9/100	0.09
11.	37%	37/100	0.37
12.	77%	77/100	0.77
13.	91%	91/100	0.91
14.	33%	33/100	0.33

59

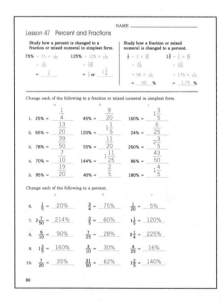

Lesson 47 Percent and Fractions

Study how a percent is changed to a fraction or mixed numeral in simplest form.

75% = 75 × 1/100   125% = 125 × 1/100

= 3/4   = 1¼

Study how a fraction or mixed numeral is changed to a percent.

¾ = ¾ × 100/1   1¾ = ¾ × 100/1

= 50 × 1/100   = 175 × 1/100

= 50 %   = 1.75 %

Change each of the following to a fraction or mixed numeral in simplest form.

	a	b	c
1.	25% = 1/4	45% = 9/20	160% = 1 3/5
2.	65% = 13/20	120% = 1 1/5	24% = 6/25
3.	78% = 39/50	55% = 11/20	260% = 2 3/5
4.	70% = 7/10	144% = 1 11/25	86% = 43/50
5.	95% = 19/20	40% = 2/5	180% = 1 4/5

Change each of the following to a percent.

	a	b	c
6.	1/5 = 20%	3/4 = 75%	1/20 = 5%
7.	2 7/50 = 214%	3/5 = 60%	1 1/5 = 120%
8.	9/10 = 90%	7/25 = 28%	2 1/4 = 225%
9.	1 3/5 = 160%	3/10 = 30%	4/25 = 16%
10.	7/20 = 35%	31/50 = 62%	1 2/5 = 140%

60

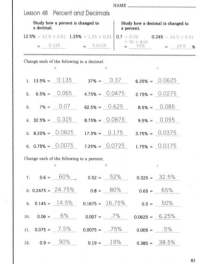

Lesson 48 Percent and Decimals

Study how a percent is changed to a decimal.

12.5% = 12.5 × 0.01   1.25% = 1.25 × 0.01

= 0.125   = 0.0125

Study how a decimal is changed to a percent.

0.7 = 0.70   0.245 = 24.5 × 0.01

= 70 × 0.01   = 24.5 %

= 70%

Change each of the following to a decimal.

	a	b	c
1.	13.5% = 0.135	37% = 0.37	6.25% = 0.0625
2.	6.5% = 0.065	4.75% = 0.0475	2.75% = 0.0275
3.	7% = 0.07	62.5% = 0.625	8.5% = 0.085
4.	32.5% = 0.325	8.75% = 0.0875	9.5% = 0.095
5.	8.25% = 0.0825	17.5% = 0.175	3.75% = 0.0375
6.	0.75% = 0.0075	7.25% = 0.0725	1.75% = 0.0175

Change each of the following to a percent.

	a	b	c
7.	0.6 = 60%	0.52 = 52%	0.325 = 32.5%
8.	0.2475 = 24.75%	0.8 = 80%	0.65 = 65%
9.	0.145 = 14.5%	0.1675 = 16.75%	0.5 = 50%
10.	0.06 = 6%	0.007 = .7%	0.0625 = 6.25%
11.	0.075 = 7.5%	0.0075 = .75%	0.005 = .5%
12.	0.9 = 90%	0.19 = 19%	0.385 = 38.5%

61

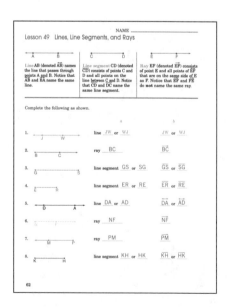

Lesson 49 Lines, Line Segments, and Rays

Line AB (denoted $\overline{AB}$) names the line that passes through points A and B. Notice that AB and BA name the same line.

Line segment CD (denoted $\overline{CD}$) consists of points C and D and all points on the line between C and D. Notice that CD and DC name the same line segment.

Ray EF (denoted $\overrightarrow{EF}$) consists of point E and all points of EF that are on the same side of E as F. Notice that EF and FE do **not** name the same ray.

Complete the following as shown.

		a	b
1.	line	JW or WJ	$\overleftrightarrow{JW}$ or $\overleftrightarrow{WJ}$
2.	ray	BC	$\overrightarrow{BC}$
3.	line segment	GS or SG	$\overline{GS}$ or $\overline{SG}$
4.	line segment	ER or RE	$\overline{ER}$ or $\overline{RE}$
5.	line	DA or AD	$\overleftrightarrow{DA}$ or $\overleftrightarrow{AD}$
6.	ray	NF	$\overrightarrow{NF}$
7.	ray	PM	$\overrightarrow{PM}$
8.	line segment	KH or HK	$\overline{KH}$ or $\overline{HK}$

62

74

ANSWER KEY

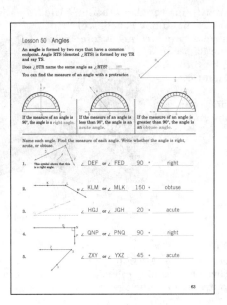

Lesson 50 Angles

An **angle** is formed by two rays that have a common endpoint. Angle RTS (denoted ∠RTS) is formed by ray TR and ray TS.

Does ∠STR name the same angle as ∠RTS?   yes

You can find the measure of an angle with a protractor.

If the measure of an angle is 90°, the angle is a right angle.

If the measure of an angle is less than 90°, the angle is an acute angle.

If the measure of an angle is greater than 90°, the angle is an obtuse angle.

Name each angle. Find the measure of each angle. Write whether the angle is right, acute, or obtuse.

1. This symbol shows that this is a right angle.
∠ DEF or ∠ FED   90 °   right

2. ∠ KLM or ∠ MLK   150 °   obtuse

3. ∠ HGJ or ∠ JGH   20 °   acute

4. ∠ QNP or ∠ PNQ   90 °   right

5. ∠ ZXY or ∠ YXZ   45 °   acute

63

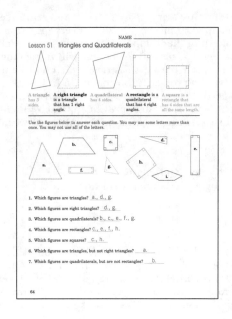

NAME _____

Lesson 51 Triangles and Quadrilaterals

A triangle has 3 sides.

A **right triangle** is a triangle that has 1 right angle.

A quadrilateral has 4 sides.

A **rectangle** is a quadrilateral that has 4 right angles.

A square is a rectangle that has 4 sides that are all the same length.

Use the figures below to answer each question. You may use some letters more than once. You may not use all of the letters.

1. Which figures are triangles? a., d., g.
2. Which figures are right triangles? d., g.
3. Which figures are quadrilaterals? b., c., e., f., g.
4. Which figures are rectangles? c., e., f., h.
5. Which figures are squares? c., h.
6. Which figures are triangles, but not right triangles? a.
7. Which figures are quadrilaterals, but are not rectangles? b.

64

McGraw-Hill Consumer Products

The skills taught in school are now available at home!
These award-winning software titles meet school guidelines and are based on
The McGraw-Hill Companies classroom software titles.

MATH GRADES 1 & 2

These math programs are a great way to teach and reinforce skills used in everyday situations. Fun, friendly characters need help with their math skills. Everyone's friend, Nubby the stubby pencil, will help kids master the math in the Numbers Quiz show. Foggy McHammer, a carpenter, needs some help building his playhouse so that all the boards will fit together! Julio Bambino's kitchen antics will surely burn his pastries if you don't help him set the clock timer correctly! We can't forget Turbo Tomato, a fruit with a passion for adventure, who needs help calculating his daredevil stunts.

Math Grades 1 & 2 use a tested, proven approach to reinforcing your child's math skills while keeping him or her intrigued with Nubby and his collection of crazy friends.

TITLE
Grade 1: Nubby's Quiz Show
Grade 2: Foggy McHammer's Treehouse

MISSION MASTERS™ MATH AND LANGUAGE ARTS

The Mission Masters™—Pauline, Rakeem, Mia, and T.J.—need your help. The Mission Masters™ are a team of young agents working for the Intelliforce Agency, a high-level cooperative whose goal is to maintain order on our rather unruly planet. From within the agency's top secret Command Control Center, the agency's central computer, M5, has detected a threat...and guess what—you're the agent assigned to the mission!

MISSION MASTERS™ MATH GRADES 3, 4, & 5

This series of exciting activities encourages young mathematicians to challenge themselves and their math skills to overcome the perils of villains and other planetary threats. Skills reinforced include: analyzing and solving real-world problems, estimation, measurements, geometry, whole numbers, fractions, graphs, and patterns.

TITLE
Grade 3: Mission Masters™ Defeat Dirty D!
Grade 4: Mission Masters™ Alien Encounter
Grade 5: Mission Masters™ Meet Mudflat Moe

MISSION MASTERS™ LANGUAGE ARTS GRADES 3, 4, & 5

This series invites children to apply their language skills to defeat unscrupulous characters and to overcome other earthly dangers. Skills reinforced include: language mechanics and usage, punctuation, spelling, vocabulary, reading comprehension, and creative writing.

TITLE
Grade 3: Mission Masters™ Freezing Frenzy
Grade 4: Mission Masters™ Network Nightmare
Grade 5: Mission Masters™ Mummy Mysteries

BASIC SKILLS BUILDER K to 2 – THE MAGIC APPLEHOUSE

At the Magic Applehouse, children discover that Abigail Appleseed runs a deliciously successful business selling apple pies, tarts, and other apple treats. Enthusiasm grows as children join in the fun of helping Abigail run her business. Along the way they'll develop computer and entrepreneurial skills to last a lifetime. They will run their own business – all while they're having bushels of fun!

TITLE
Basic Skills Builder –The Magic Applehouse

TEST PREP – SCORING HIGH

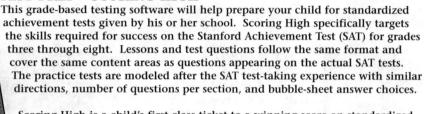

This grade-based testing software will help prepare your child for standardized achievement tests given by his or her school. Scoring High specifically targets the skills required for success on the Stanford Achievement Test (SAT) for grades three through eight. Lessons and test questions follow the same format and cover the same content areas as questions appearing on the actual SAT tests. The practice tests are modeled after the SAT test-taking experience with similar directions, number of questions per section, and bubble-sheet answer choices.

Scoring High is a child's first-class ticket to a winning score on standardized achievement tests!

TITLE
Grades 3 to 5: Scoring High Test Prep
Grades 6 to 8: Scoring High Test Prep

SCIENCE

Mastering the principles of both physical and life science has never been so FUN for kids grades six and above as it is while they are exploring McGraw-Hill's edutainment software!

TITLE
Grades 6 & up: Life Science
Grades 8 & up: Physical Science

REFERENCE

The National Museum of Women in the Arts has teamed with McGraw-Hill Consumer Products to bring you this superb collection available for your enjoyment on CD-ROM.

This special collection is a visual diary of 200 women artists from the Renaissance to the present, spanning 500 years of creativity.

You will discover the art of women who excelled in all the great art movements of history. Artists who pushed the boundaries of abstract, genre, landscape, narrative, portrait, and still-life styles; as well as artists forced to push the societal limits placed on women through the ages.

TITLE
Women in the Arts

Most titles for Windows 3.1™, Windows '95™ & '98™, and Macintosh™.

Visit us on the Internet at:

www.MHkids.com

Or call 800-298-4119 for your local retailer.

McGraw-Hill Consumer Products

All our workbooks meet school curriculum guidelines and correspond to
The McGraw-Hill Companies classroom textbooks.

SPECTRUM SERIES

DOLCH Sight Word Activities

The DOLCH Sight Word Activities Workbooks use the classic Dolch list of 220 basic vocabulary words that make up from 50% to 75% of all reading matter that children ordinarily encounter. Since these words are ordinarily recognized on sight, they are called *sight words*. Volume 1 includes 110 sight words. Volume 2 covers the remainder of the list. Over 160 pages.

TITLE	ISBN	PRICE
Grades K-1 Vol. 1	1-57768-429-X	$9.95
Grades K-1 Vol. 2	1-57768-439-7	$9.95

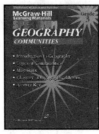

GEOGRAPHY

Full-color, three-part lessons strengthen geography knowledge and map reading skills. Focusing on five geographic themes including location, place, human/environmental interaction, movement, and regions. Over 150 pages. Glossary of geographical terms and answer key included.

TITLE	ISBN	PRICE
Gr 3, Communities	1-57768-153-3	$7.95
Gr 4, Regions	1-57768-154-1	$7.95
Gr 5, USA	1-57768-155-X	$7.95
Gr 6, World	1-57768-156-8	$7.95

MATH

Features easy-to-follow instructions that give students a clear path to success. This series has comprehensive coverage of the basic skills, helping children to master math fundamentals. Over 150 pages. Answer key included.

TITLE	ISBN	PRICE
Grade 1	1-57768-111-8	$6.95
Grade 2	1-57768-112-6	$6.95
Grade 3	1-57768-113-4	$6.95
Grade 4	1-57768-114-2	$6.95
Grade 5	1-57768-115-0	$6.95
Grade 6	1-57768-116-9	$6.95
Grade 7	1-57768-117-7	$6.95
Grade 8	1-57768-118-5	$6.95

PHONICS

Provides everything children need to build multiple skills in language. Focusing on phonics, structural analysis, and dictionary skills, this series also offers creative ideas for using phonics and word study skills in other language arts. Over 200 pages. Answer key included.

TITLE	ISBN	PRICE
Grade K	1-57768-120-7	$6.95
Grade 1	1-57768-121-5	$6.95
Grade 2	1-57768-122-3	$6.95
Grade 3	1-57768-123-1	$6.95
Grade 4	1-57768-124-X	$6.95
Grade 5	1-57768-125-8	$6.95
Grade 6	1-57768-126-6	$6.95

SPECTRUM SERIES – continued

READING

This full-color series creates an enjoyable reading environment, even for below-average readers. Each book contains captivating content, colorful characters, and compelling illustrations, so children are eager to find out what happens next. Over 150 pages. Answer key included.

TITLE	ISBN	PRICE
Grade K	1-57768-130-4	$6.95
Grade 1	1-57768-131-2	$6.95
Grade 2	1-57768-132-0	$6.95
Grade 3	1-57768-133-9	$6.95
Grade 4	1-57768-134-7	$6.95
Grade 5	1-57768-135-5	$6.95
Grade 6	1-57768-136-3	$6.95

SPELLING

This full-color series links spelling to reading and writing and increases skills in words and meanings, consonant and vowel spellings, and proofreading practice. Over 200 pages. Speller dictionary and answer key included.

TITLE	ISBN	PRICE
Grade 1	1-57768-161-4	$7.95
Grade 2	1-57768-162-2	$7.95
Grade 3	1-57768-163-0	$7.95
Grade 4	1-57768-164-9	$7.95
Grade 5	1-57768-165-7	$7.95
Grade 6	1-57768-166-5	$7.95

WRITING

Lessons focus on creative and expository writing using clearly stated objectives and pre-writing exercises. Eight essential reading skills are applied. Activities include main idea, sequence, comparison, detail, fact and opinion, cause and effect, and making a point. Over 130 pages. Answer key included.

TITLE	ISBN	PRICE
Grade 1	1-57768-141-X	$6.95
Grade 2	1-57768-142-8	$6.95
Grade 3	1-57768-143-6	$6.95
Grade 4	1-57768-144-4	$6.95
Grade 5	1-57768-145-2	$6.95
Grade 6	1-57768-146-0	$6.95
Grade 7	1-57768-147-9	$6.95
Grade 8	1-57768-148-7	$6.95

TEST PREP
From the Nation's #1 Testing Company

Prepares children to do their best on current editions of the five major standardized tests. Activities reinforce test-taking skills through examples, tips, practice, and timed exercises. Subjects include reading, math, and language. Over 150 pages. Answer key included.

TITLE	ISBN	PRICE
Grade 1	1-57768-101-0	$8.95
Grade 2	1-57768-102-9	$8.95
Grade 3	1-57768-103-7	$8.95
Grade 4	1-57768-104-5	$8.95
Grade 5	1-57768-105-3	$8.95
Grade 6	1-57768-106-1	$8.95
Grade 7	1-57768-107-X	$8.95
Grade 8	1-57768-108-8	$8.95

Visit us on the Internet at:

www.MHkids.com

Or call 800-298-4119 for your local retailer.

The McGraw·Hill

JUNIOR ACADEMIC SERIES

CERTIFICATE OF ACCOMPLISHMENT

THIS CERTIFIES THAT

HAS SUCCESSFULLY COMPLETED
THE JUNIOR ACADEMIC'S™

GRADE 6
MATH
WORKBOOK.

CONGRATULATIONS AND KEEP UP THE GOOD WORK!

The McGraw·Hill Companies

Publisher